"Toni, don't look at me like that."

Cay's voice was husky as he gazed down at her. Slowly he brushed his thumb across her lower lip. "You're encouraging me to take unfair advantage of you."

"I know," she murmured, unable to move away. His words, his touch were doing crazy things to her.

"I've been heroic on a couple of other occasions, but I think this well of chivalry you've tapped is fast running dry."

Toni slid her hands up his bare chest. "So stop playing the hero. . . ."

*First published in Great Britain 1989 by
Mills & Boon Limited, Eton House, 18–24 Paradise Road,
Richmond, Surrey, TW9 1SR*

© Shirley Larson 1986

ISBN 0 263 76764 7

21–8912

Made and printed in Great Britain

1

"YOU'RE WORRYING," Toni Pereola's girlfriend, Liz, said from the passenger seat in the van. "You'll get a frown line between your eyes."

As Toni guided the van in and out of the Key West, Florida traffic, she narrowly avoided a Volkswagen being driven with the same panache. "This is ridiculous. They limit the number of cars on the island of Bermuda," she muttered. "Why can't they do that here?"

"And stop the tourist trade? Not likely. Mike warned us the traffic would be worse on the weekend—" Liz Harris shot a look at Toni. "Oops, sorry."

"You can mention his name," Toni said dryly. "I won't fall on the floor and beat my chest in agony."

"Listen," Liz put in quickly, "the world is full of men—"

"If you think that thought is going to make me cheer up, you're wrong." Liz turned her head away to stare out into the twilight, and Toni felt a stab of contrition. In a softer tone, she said, "I just wish the big dope had waited another month before deciding that gentlemen prefer blondes. Are you sure you can handle that big amp by yourself?"

Liz cheered up instantly. "Not to worry. I've been pumping iron for the last two weeks. Everything is under control, chief."

Dear Liz. Sweet, idealistic Liz. So very young. At twenty-nine, Toni felt light years away from Liz's twenty-one.

She wasn't taken in by Michael's charm, you were. It was you, streetwise, cool, smart Toni from the Bronx who fell for the muscle-bound bum, in Fort Lauderdale, no less, on the beach under an August moon.

She should have known better. The worst of it was, she was more worried about who was going to haul the equipment in and out of the van than she was about her broken heart. Mike could lift anything...and did. He'd been their lone roadie for the last three concerts they'd done in Miami.

She should have known better than to trust a man. She should have learned that lesson twenty years ago on the day her oldest brother, Rob, told her to look the other way and stole her piece of cake. She hadn't cared about the cake. She had cared about the way her brother had laughed at her gullibility. Red lights flashed in her face. Instinctively Toni hit the brakes.

"Now what?" Liz strained forward in her seat to see.

"Traffic has stopped completely."

"What time did you tell Mr. Sinclair we'd be at the dock?"

"Six-thirty."

"What time is it now?"

"Six-twenty."

"What time does the concert start?"

"Seven-thirty."

"Are we in trouble?"

"What do you think?" Toni leaned back against the vinyl seat and felt her T-shirt turn into instant glue. The evening air was cool, but she felt hot and prickly. The drive from Miami had taken six hours instead of five, and now they were stuck like a beached whale in this traffic jam.

"How far away are we?"

"Well, we can't be too far. I can see the Gulf up ahead."

Liz beamed. "If we're that close, we can stop worrying. What's ten minutes here or there?"

"Ten minutes here or there might cost us this job. Sinclair is a perfectionist. If we mess up on this first gig, he might decide to cancel us out of the other two. If he does that, we can kiss the equipment goodbye. The bank will repossess it."

"He won't cancel us. You're the best free-lance sound engineer in southern Florida."

"Unfortunately, he doesn't think so. We weren't his first choice for this job. We weren't even his third choice."

The traffic began to move again, crawling at a nerve-racking pace. Toni tried to practice the mind control she'd learned while growing up with four brothers and three sisters, but it wasn't working.

Fifteen minutes later, relieved and apprehensive at the same time, Toni pulled into the parking lot at Mallory Dock. They were only a few minutes behind schedule. Maybe, just maybe, she could get set up without delaying the concert.

She scanned the pier. The crowd was growing in anticipation of the concert to come.

Toni's mind worked furiously. The amp first. Get it on the dolly and pray that, by some miracle, she and Liz could push it over the sand to the pier. Then, bring out the two auxiliary speakers and the monitors for the two guitar players. The drums were already set up. Oh, Lord. Three crash cymbals. Her eardrums were going to take a beating. And worse, everyone else's ears would be suffering too, and because it was a live concert, there wasn't a darn thing she could do about it. Drums were the snaggletoothed dragon in the life of every sound engineer.

She sighed, thinking of the lovely recording studio she'd worked in two weeks before, where they'd had the most beautiful sound booth for the drums. Tonight's gig, on a scale of one to ten, rated a minus two. On top of everything else, they would have to please the great rock star.

A man stepped out of the crowd and headed toward them. Cay Sinclair was as wide shouldered, slim hipped and good-looking as his publicity stills. More so. There was a maturity in his face that hadn't been evident five years ago when he'd quit giving concerts, a maturity combined with . . . magnetism—sheer, unmitigated sexual magnetism.

I should have stayed in Miami, Toni thought.

She had been crazy to listen to Liz's pleading for a chance to work on the island where her elusive sometime-boyfriend ran a charter fishing boat, crazy to let her blighted romance with Mike send her running to the southernmost point of the United States, crazy to contract for this assignment. But to sit around in Miami and wait for another job would have been sheer folly... especially since this one offered the opportunity to flee from Mike.

"Oh, Lord," Liz muttered. "Here he comes and he doesn't look happy. I'll stay in the van and let you handle this one, chief."

"Thanks." Toni felt hot and edgy, and the last thing she needed was to spend her precious few minutes before the concert in a confrontation with Cay Sinclair.

She got out and met him at the back of the van. He stood looking at her disheveled hair, her cropped T-shirt and her short shorts, which wore a dollop of mustard from lunch. Then, the man who wrote lyrics of soaring beauty and stunning sensuality to the music he composed said, "You're late."

She had to give him credit. He was quick. "We got held up in traffic."

"You should have left Miami sooner." His cool eyes played over her, impersonally cataloging each individual feature of her face and figure. In the twilight, she couldn't see what color was hidden in the dark depths of his eyes. What she could see was his well-defined, narrow nose, his finely shaped ears and his often-photographed, sensual mouth. There was a look about him as if he were more knowledgeable of the world and its foibles than any man should be. "Was there someone you didn't want to leave?"

He didn't even know her.

She gritted her teeth. "Actually there was someone I *did* want to leave."

Now why had she said that? She'd been determined to hold her tongue and be pleasant. The man had a bad effect on her. "We're wasting time standing here talking. I'm ready to start setting up."

"Where's your roadie?"

"He couldn't make it."

Cay Sinclair looked as if he were putting two and two together and coming up with four at roughly the speed of light. "Mixing business with pleasure, were you?"

Toni replied in a cool tone, "I have a friend with me. We'll manage." She could see that he was angry.

"I'll talk to the security man, and you can pull out of that parking place and back in right next to the pier and unload directly onto the blacktop. Give me your main extension cord. I'll go plug it in to the source I got permission for you to use."

She wanted to ask him if she should salute when she finished, but she knew it wouldn't be wise to antagonize him further. Besides, he'd done her a favor. It wasn't his job to worry about the power supply, it was hers. And she had been worried. For an outdoor concert, she usually scouted out a power source a day ahead of time and then spent twenty-four hours praying that the line would take the load. A blown fuse was a major catastrophe.

She jumped up into the back of the van, and conscious of Sinclair leaning against one of the open doors watching her, she grabbed the cord quickly and handed it to him. "I appreciate your taking care of this."

"My pleasure," he said, cool as ice.

She'd come prepared to like him. She'd seen him once in concert. It had been at the last concert he'd given in

New York City. She'd gone to Central Park and she'd stood watching him, enthralled. She didn't feel enthralled now. Why was it that reality never matched her dreams?

Against her will, her eyes clung to him, watching him move lithely away.

Liz's red head appeared from behind the door. "Wow! Didn't I tell you the world was full of men? Wouldn't it be wonderful if it were full of men like him?"

For no reason that she could think of, Toni was annoyed. "Come on, let's get to work."

Slowly, expertly, Toni backed the van as close to the pier as she could. A minute later, while loading the amp onto the cart, Liz said dreamily, "He's such a fox."

"Control yourself and think of Tommy. He's a fox, too. Remember?"

"I wonder what his secret is."

Toni didn't have to ask which "he" Liz was talking about. "He has an M.B.A. from Harvard," she joked in a dry tone.

"Does he?"

Toni shook her head. Liz simply couldn't always keep up with her weird sense of humor. "No, of course not. I think he has a Master's from Juilliard."

"A Master's from Juilliard and charm besides? He must be dynamite."

"He's one of the best all-around talents in the music business," Toni told her wryly. "Even though he no longer makes personal appearances, he still records, and his records continue to sell. That's supposed to be an impossibility. Help me with that Pierson amp, will you?"

Toni hopped up inside the van and began to jockey the equipment around, but her mind was on Sinclair. Had she antagonized him? She couldn't afford to do that, not this trip. She would be working with him for the next three weeks. He was overseeing the four productions—one each week for the next month—that the Key West Association to Promote the Arts had agreed to sponsor for the Celebrate the Romance of Key West Days. They were using local artists for the first three concerts, and Sinclair would be doing the final one. He spent two months each winter in Key West and had volunteered his services for these concerts—otherwise the nonprofit Key West Association could never have afforded a man with such a formidable reputation in the music world.

After she'd signed the contract with the Association, Sinclair had called her to discuss the sound equipment he thought would be needed for each concert. His voice had sounded cool, and she knew he wasn't wildly enthusiastic about her work, but she'd thought once she'd done a concert, he'd relax. That was another dream bubble burst.

Tonight he looked carefully casual in faded jeans and a white shirt, but the charisma that had put his name and his music at the top of the charts for three years before he was thirty hadn't diminished a thimbleful. How old was he? Somewhere around thirty-five now, she supposed.

A man in his prime.

Stop thinking dumb thoughts, Toni, and get this show on the road. You have work to do.

"Hey, is this the chick that's doing our sound? She's cool, man."

Key West's answer to Elvis Presley, a guitar dangling from a strap around his neck, came swaggering over to watch Toni work at the mixing board. He was one of the Princes of Conch, the rock group giving the evening's concert.

He leaned over her shoulder. "Are you sure you know how to run this thing?"

"Quite sure. Was there something you wanted?"

"Yeah, there's something I want. You."

She supposed he thought the dark, suggestive look he gave her was a turn-on.

"Leave her alone," a male with a voice the texture of granite said from somewhere behind her.

Toni couldn't see Cay Sinclair, but she could see the young man's reaction to Cay's presence.

"Hey, man, no problem. Everything's cool. You and the chick got something going, I wouldn't want to interfere with that, no way." As easily as he'd appeared, he melted back into the crowd.

Angrily Toni twirled around on her stool. Sinclair was ready for her. "Going to tell me that you fight your own battles?"

"Something like that. I'm used to taking care of myself."

"Are you?" The words taunted gently.

"Yes."

"Like you did in Miami, I presume?"

She felt the red color rush up to fill her cheeks. "Excuse me. I have to get back to work."

SHE LOOKED FAMILIAR. That notion haunted Cay like the name of a song he was trying to remember and couldn't, or a tune he was composing that just wouldn't come out right. He'd talked to her on the phone and something about her voice had made him picture her as an over-endowed bleached blonde. He hadn't expected this trim little five-foot-five ball of fire, who swung along in black ballet slippers and black shorts with a cool, professional smile. Professional? Was she really a pro or was it an act? A moment before, she'd been totally absorbed in her work, her brows drawn together in a frown.

Sound Design, her T-shirt said, and underneath it, her feminine curves moved with a subtle bounce that proved the medium was the message. She was a "sound design"—the most attractively packaged bundle of trouble he'd seen in ages. And she was going to be trouble. He was sure of it. A woman doing a man's job was always trouble. It put her in the realm of the young punk he'd just sent away.

Cay had been apprehensive when he'd learned the Key West Association had signed a woman to do the sound, but he hadn't been in a position to say anything. He was a consultant, after all, not the guiding force. He'd have to watch her.

He looked out over the ocean. A few boats were already gathering. He'd made arrangements with the Coast Guard so that people could come and watch the concert from the water if they wished. He hoped there wouldn't be a flotilla. He didn't think there would.

At twenty minutes after seven, when the dark-haired fireball had run five sound checks and repositioned the mikes four times, he shook his head. She was a fierce little perfectionist who was going to make waves wherever she went. The Princes were already bored with her repeatedly making them play a measure and stop, then sing a measure and stop, but the audience was loving it. No, maybe what they loved was seeing the way she moved. He was getting addicted himself to watching how her shorts tightened around her nicely formed bottom when she bent over a mike and leaned down to check a connection.

The music, when it started, was not quite as ear-splitting as he'd thought it would be. A very real part of the group's appeal came from Toni's expert handling of the sound. Her head was constantly bent over the mixing board, her short black hair pushed against her cheek by the headphones. The bass guitarist used a stroke-and-slap technique on his strings that should have raised the hair on his neck...and didn't. Toni had discreetly toned it down, taken out the pop and splat, leaving a nice percussive ping that pleased rather than irritated. The woman had a good ear. He would have enjoyed having her with him in the days when he toured. She was a fine sound engineer and a hell of a lot better looking than DeSanto.

The Princes were scheduled to take an intermission from their royal music making halfway through the concert—around eight-thirty. Cay waited for that intermission with an impatience he couldn't remember feeling in years. He'd long since learned to cultivate patience. Producing required a serenity that roughly equaled Buddha's. But tonight he was impatient. He wanted the kids to stop playing, and he wanted Toni's shiny black head to lift from the mixing board. He wanted to see if her eyes really were silver and as large as they had seemed or if that had been a trick of the light.

The vociferous applause from the teenage crowd on the beach and the bleat of boat horns told him that the Princes were taking their break. He waited until the young men put down their guitars and then swung a leg over the rope barrier he had ordered erected, nodded at the security guard he'd hired and headed for Toni.

Meanwhile, realizing that the first half of the concert was over and that no major disaster had occurred, Toni lifted her perspiration-dampened face from the board. Now if she could just get through the next hour without anything going wrong...

She wasn't going to manage that. Something had already gone wrong. Sinclair was on the prowl.

He strolled toward her, the band's spotlights flashing on him, turning him alternating shades of red, blue and green. She liked him best in blue. The Blue Shadow. He wasn't the Green Hornet. His nose was too... classic.

He stopped short of her, his face in the shadows. "I'll get you something to drink. What would you like?"

"Nothing, thanks."

"Nothing?"

She tilted her head to look up into his dark-shadowed, famous face. "I'm not thirsty."

Not interested was the message she was trying to give him. He'd lay odds to that. She seemed to be looking right through him, her expression was of complete indifference. Her partner stood just a few feet away, watching, but Cay didn't give a damn if the whole world looked on while he made a fool of himself. That was extremely odd. He'd never felt that way before.

"The concert's going well. You know your business."

"Thank you, Mr. Sinclair." She paused, and he sensed the rapier coming even before it pierced him. "So do you."

He felt the swift rise of anger. Had he sounded that patronizing? He hadn't meant to. And yet he probably had, even without knowing it.

Her eyes *were* silver, moon-touched, mirrors that gave away none of the secrets of her mind. In contrast to her dark clothes, her eyes shimmered with light. They hypnotized him, making it impossible for him to turn away.

The sixty-cycle hum of the Pierson amp screamed in Toni's ear like a siren. Was he ever going to go away? She could feel Liz watching them both. Didn't the man understand? *I don't care for a drink, Mr. Sinclair. I'm not thirsty. Find some other female to charm. This one is overworked and underpaid.*

"I've asked the guard to stay until you've packed up."

"Thank you."

He had to ease the pressure—let her think she could lower her defenses. He'd make her believe he'd gotten her hands-off message. Nodding casually to her, he gave her assistant a wave of his hand and sauntered back down the pier.

"You should be commissioned." Liz's face had pinkened, and she looked charmingly flustered.

Toni lifted an eyebrow. "Commissioned?"

"You know, sent to a mental ward."

"You mean committed," Toni said, smiling.

Liz wasn't fazed at being corrected. "You must be crazy to let a man like that walk away from you."

"No." Toni shook her head and dragged her eyes away from Cay Sinclair's retreating figure. She remembered reading that he'd been married, and that the marriage had crumbled under the pressure of differing careers. After his divorce, photographs of him had appeared in fan magazines, showing a woman dressed in a pink satin jumpsuit standing beside him and gazing at him adoringly. The captions had read, Sinclair No Longer Singing the Blues. "Avoiding a lethally packaged male like Cay Sinclair isn't crazy. A man like that can be hazardous to your health."

Liz rolled her eyes. "Would just a tiny touch of the flu be too much to ask?"

Toni laughed and shook her head.

The sound of her low, throaty laugh drifted across the water. Sinclair turned around and saw them. Toni had her face turned up to that Amazonian assistant of hers. They looked like Robin Hood and Little John. Toni was definitely Robin, the brains of the operation. Yes, Robin Hood was a good comparison. Toni carried her own quiver of arrows. He'd felt their sting only minutes ago.

The Princes returned and the concert wore on to the finish. They played heavy-metal rock, and to Sinclair's ears, it sounded old-fashioned. He'd been through that era. Musically, he was ready for something new, something lighter, something more intelligent. He realized suddenly those were the same qualities that he'd been looking for in a woman. Funny. He hadn't known that until tonight.

The Princes took their last bow and were promptly overrun by young female autograph hunters. Sinclair waited until Toni and Liz had finished rolling up cords and packing gear. As he'd guessed, there were too many things to carry back to the van in one trip.

He stepped over the rope cordoning off their area and took the handles of the dolly from Liz. "I'll take this. You get the rest." He circled around and headed toward the van before either woman could protest.

"Now isn't he a peach to help us?" Liz said, flashing a beatific smile at his retreating back.

"He's a regular pie à la mode. Watch the end of that extension cord. It's live. Here, plug this dummy into it. I'll take this load back and go unplug everything. No, don't lift that in," she shouted to Sinclair. "Everything has to be packed in order."

And everything was packed in order, Sinclair thought as he watched her pick and choose and stack. An amp went on the carpet-covered floor in the far corner of the van, its twin went beside it. The mixing board went next. It was anchored to the side with a strap. The mike heads went into a felt box. The carpenter apron went in last, hung over a hook on the inside of the back door.

Toni slammed the door shut and locked it.

To the soft Key West night, he said, "Have dinner with me."

That brought Toni's head up. Before she could articulate the "no" that shone out of her eyes, he quickly added, "I have some things I want to discuss with you."

She didn't believe him, not for a minute. But suppose he did mean it? She'd make a fool of herself if she attached more importance to a dinner invitation than there was. "You can call me tomorrow."

"It would be easier to talk about it now," he said smoothly.

What could it hurt to have dinner at his expense, temptation whispered. *Think of that bag of stale potato chips and that half of a ham sandwich with too much mustard on it that you saved from lunch. Is that really what you want to eat tonight?*

As if he'd read her mind, he said, "Tujones is famous for its broiled yellowtail snapper. Do you like seafood?"

Asking her if she liked seafood was like asking the sun if it meant to come up. "Yes, very much."

Liz said quickly, "I'll drive the van home. Tommy's probably already there waiting for me. You go ahead."

Toni glanced down at her bare legs. "I'm not dressed properly."

He didn't want her to go home and change her clothes—and her mind along with them.

"You look fine," Sinclair assured her, taking her arm with his long, lean fingers, which looked as if they'd been designed especially to glide over the keys of a piano. Liz gunned the van and tore off, taking away Toni's last line of retreat.

She thought that, at the very least, he would help her into a red Ferrari. Instead, he asked her if she minded walking to Tujones. Walking was far preferable to being squeezed into a sports car beside him. She told him no, she didn't mind . . . and then realized she would have been better off in an automobile with the gear shift between them. Going on foot through a Key West night down Duval Street was not an activity conducive to business discussions. Palm trees whispered in a strange counterpoint to the laughter that broke out sporadically from the outdoor bars interspersed along Duval among the houses and stores. A cool night breeze caressed her face, and Sinclair's fingers on her elbow felt . . . right.

As they walked, someone jostled her from behind. When the person came around in front of them, she saw it was a man of medium height, but his features were hidden by the brim of a ridiculous felt hat that looked as if it had flown straight off the pages of *The Three Musketeers* to land on the fellow's head, drooping orange and purple feathers and all.

"Hello, Cay."

Toni tensed. There was something about the man that made her feel she was being accosted. The stranger stood in front of Sinclair, blocking his path and bringing his lithe stride to a halt. The feather wearer swung to her. "And Miss Pereola. How nice to see you."

"What are you doing here?" Sinclair said in a brittle tone.

"Is that any way to talk to an old comrade in arms?"

Cay grabbed her and did a sidestep, and before she knew it, Toni had been whisked into one of the many boutiques that lined the street.

"You have rather . . . unique friends."

Cay quickly glanced around the shop as if searching for lurking figures of vengeance behind the counters.

Then his gaze settled on her. Green. His eyes were the green of expensive crystal.

"What did you do to him, Mr. Sinclair? Refuse to put up the money to back his nonexistent talent? Or toss his sister out of your motel room in Keokuk?"

He didn't move, but his eyes flared, and she knew her shot had been straight on target. "Neither, as it happens." Toni looked up at him, not quite sure of his mood. He sounded amiable enough, but there was a sliver of steel in his voice. "He seemed to know you."

Shock and surprise made her skin burn. "I've never seen him before in my life."

"I wonder if that's true," he murmured, his eyes on hers.

She was angry and disturbed in a way she'd promised herself she would never be again when Mike had walked out. "Would you like to rescind your invitation?"

Had she thought there was steel in his voice? Somehow, that hardest of metals had now shifted to his eyes. Green steel. Interesting. As a fencing match, her eyes to his, it was a draw.

"No."

Not particularly caring whether he followed her or not, she turned to walk out of the boutique. When they started down the street again, his hand found her elbow. "Is he gone?" she asked carelessly.

"He seems to be." His tone of voice told her he didn't want to discuss the subject.

When they walked in the door at Tujones, the hostess's eyes met Sinclair's over Toni's head. "A table for two? Right this way."

She led them to a secluded corner in the back, away from the windows, whose old-fashioned shutters were pulled up and open to the street.

"Sit with your back to the wall," Toni advised Cay Sinclair, with tongue-in-cheek. "If Wild Bill Hickok had done that he wouldn't be dead now." She lifted her shoulders in comic resignation. "Well, he'd be dead by now, but he wouldn't have died from a gunshot wound."

His smile shocked, surprised and pleased her.

"You do have a fund of the most useful information," he said, taking the chair she'd indicated. It was exactly where he wanted to be. If anyone approached, he would see them first.

The restaurant was casual, reminiscent of a barn with its exposed wooden walls and rafters. Many of the patrons wore shorts just as she did, and Toni didn't feel as out of place as she had expected to. After the wine steward brought her requested glass of Chablis, and they had placed their dinner order, she found herself relaxing.

"You said you wanted to talk about the concerts."

Cay Sinclair leaned back in his chair. "I believe I told you I'd have my own sound crew come in for the final concert."

"That was the agreement." Tensely she fingered her glass, wondering what it was he was going to say. After their initial antagonism, he'd been complimentary tonight. Had he decided to cut her out of the remaining concerts after all?

"I've changed my mind. I'd like you to do it."

Somewhere in another part of the restaurant, someone was playing a Spanish guitar softly but with passion. Before she had time to breathe or think, he began
talking again.

"We'll renegotiate terms. I'm willing to pay you five
hundred dollars for that one night."

"Five hundred—" She broke off. "You're doing it as
a benefit. You can't pay me five hundred dollars for a
concert that is going to net you exactly zero."

"I'll be the judge of that."

She looked up at him, her face warm, her eyes brilliant. "Don't try to buy me, Mr. Sinclair. I'm not for
sale."

"I wasn't aware I was buying you. I thought I was
buying your expertise and your . . . equipment."

Later, in a cooler moment, he would curse himself for
a very large tactical error. But at that instant, he
couldn't keep his eyes from drifting down over her chin,
her shoulders, her breasts.

Cool as permafrost, she lifted her wineglass, drained
it and set it back down on the table. "The answer is
no . . . to everything."

"You haven't even been asked yet."

"Haven't I?"

She sounded cool, but anger had flushed her cheeks
and neck. Cay swore silently to himself. He would give
anything to take that look off her face. But she hadn't
run, at least not yet. "Don't go."

"You are psychic, aren't you?"

He leaned forward. "Listen to me. Tonight you mixed
sound for three guitars and a bass, and you were paid
one hundred dollars. When you do my sound, you'll be

mixing a Rhodes Chroma, an E-mu 4060 digital key-board and a Memorymoog Plus on some songs. On others, I'll be using an old minimoog I'm fond of and a Hohner clavinet that gives me a sound I can't get from anything else. I simply took what you earned tonight and multiplied it by five. Would you consider working for me if I multiplied it by two instead and offered you a fee I consider grossly unfair to you?"

The flush faded and she relaxed back in her chair. "An old minimoog?"

He nodded.

"I haven't mixed sound for one of those in ages. How about . . . two and a half times?"

"Two hundred and fifty? I'm still getting a bargain."

"Well, bargains are hard to find these days, aren't they?"

It was a truce, and he knew it. "Increasingly hard to find. You'll do it?" She nodded, and feeling triumphant and happier than he had in a long time, he lifted his wineglass to toast their agreement.

A few minutes later the snapper came. It was deco-rated with parsley and lemon and was accompanied by side dishes of beans and rice to mix together. She was glad she hadn't gotten up and dashed dramatically out of the dining room. The food was wonderful—and she told him so.

"I'm glad you enjoyed it. Would you like some Key Lime pie?"

She gave him a half smile. "If I did, I would have eaten it first."

"First?"

"I come from a large family, and I learned very early in life that if you wanted that portion of your dessert sitting next to your plate, you ate it before somebody else did."

"What did your mother think about that?"

Toni's eyes were alive with laughter. "She just gave up and said if we didn't eat our pie, we wouldn't get any meat and potatoes."

"Smart lady. It must run in the family. Does engineering run in the family, too?"

"I suppose you could say that. I had an uncle who liked ham radio. He had a special room for his equipment that was off-limits to everybody. I used to sneak in and fall asleep on the couch. He'd come in and find me, and every time he did, I had to memorize the code signals for six letters of the alphabet." She shrugged, her mouth curving in a smile. "Eventually I learned them all. He helped me get my novice license and from there I graduated to working with the electronic equipment that was around—mostly amps and keyboards."

"Do you have a degree in sound engineering?"

She shook her head. "I went to school for two years, but I dropped out when—" She stopped speaking and pulled her eyes away from his. What an idiot she was to sit and babble her life story to him.

"When?" His eyes dared her to tell him.

"When I decided I didn't want to go to school anymore. Mr. Sinclair, it's been delightful, really it has. I hate to eat and run, but I must go."

He threw a bill on the table that she knew would have paid for several yellow-snapper dinners—and probably the boat that went out to catch them. "I'll walk you home."

"That's not necessary."

"I think it is."

"No—"

"And if you run into D'Artagnan on your way home? What then?"

"I can take care of myself."

"Then think about protecting me."

She did and it was an intriguing thought. Maybe he was in danger, and it would be better if they walked home together.

No, it wasn't better. It was much, much worse. For one thing, it was darker; and for another, he didn't take her arm or her hand. He didn't touch her at all. But after an entire evening of talking to him while watching his face as he tried not to react to the outrageous things she said and trying to control her reactions to the outrageous things he said, she . . . missed him. Yes, that was it. He walked next to her, but mentally he wasn't there. He had withdrawn. She risked a sidelong glance at him—and understood at once why he was so quiet. He was as alert as a cat watching . . . what?

Liz had a friend who had a rich friend who had a house in Key West. It was not a modest home. It was two stories and had the traditional balcony found on the old houses in the area. As they walked closer and Toni identified it as the place she was staying, Sinclair cast an anxious glance up at that balcony.

He looked around and then went up the steps with her to the front door. "Where's Liz?"

She realized then that he'd been looking for the van. She turned to face him. In the dark, he seemed very close. "Probably with Tommy."

"Does she make a habit of staying out all night?"

"She hasn't seen him for quite a while." Toni unlocked the door and turned around. He was outlined by the streetlight, his hair satiny black, his face hidden. He appeared the stuff of dreams—a wide-shouldered, slim-hipped male, standing a foot away from her, as evocative, as wonderful and as unreal as a song. "Good night, Mr. Sinclair. Thank you for dinner."

"It was my pleasure. Good night, Toni."

She stood still, letting the sight of him etch itself into her memory, feeling a sudden sense of unreality. She couldn't be standing there inviting him to kiss her, yet it was vitally important that she stand very still and not move. So very, very important . . .

"Be sure the doors are all locked before you go to bed." His low, familiar voice sounded cool, bland. He turned and ran lithely down the steps and was halfway up the street before she realized he was gone.

She watched him walk away from her with stunned amazement. She'd been a twenty-four carat fool. Gritting her teeth, she opened the door.

Well, so much for the legendary charm of the legendary rock star. She had expected at least a token pass. After all, he'd looked willing enough at the pier and in the restaurant.

She closed the door behind her and flicked on the light. Some men had no sense of chivalry whatsoever. He could have at least tried to kiss her.

The more she thought about it, the more annoyed she got. She went around the house turning on lights and muttering about Mr. Superstar Sinclair under her breath, conveniently forgetting that she'd been determined to discourage him at all costs.

And when she had finally locked the front door, she felt the old, aching emptiness start. She needed comfort. She needed to immerse herself in warm water and forget how she'd practically thrown herself at a man who was as much out of her reach as the one in the moon. She needed a bath.

AS HE STEPPED AWAY from Toni's house, Cay's eyes swept the darkness, but he knew Torgen wasn't there. He'd seen the man melt into the shadows when he'd turned around after telling Toni good-night. His ruse had worked. She was safe.

He walked slowly down the street, oblivious to the warmth and silkiness of the night. He was thinking about what had happened, how he'd felt Torgen's presence the minute he had stepped out of the restaurant with Toni. The sixth sense he'd developed over the last few years about Torgen was as sensitive as ever. Cay's hair had gone up on the back of his neck and his skin had prickled. He'd spotted Torgen's shadow moving behind them as they retraced their steps on Duval.

Torgen had followed them all the way home. He'd considered telling Toni about him and asking her to let him stay the night to protect her, but from her reaction to him, he knew that was impossible. Besides, Torgen wanted him, not Toni. And the less involved Cay appeared to be with Toni, the safer she was.

The nagging thought that he hadn't wanted to let surface came to the top.

How had Torgen known her name?

Cay let himself into his house—the house he had used as a winter retreat for the last three years. It had always been so good to get away from New York City for a while. Now, with Torgen here . . .

Morry, his manager, was dozing in the overstuffed chair in the corner.

"Wake up, Morry, and go to bed."

Morry gave him a dazed look and grunted. "Sure."

When Cay sank into the U-shaped couch in front of the fireplace, Morry said, "Aren't you going to bed?"

"Later. I've got some thinking to do."

"How'd the concert go?"

Cay grimaced.

"I thought so." Morry shook his head. "Glad I didn't go. You want something to drink?"

"I could use something if you're in the mood to pour."

Morry went around the corner to the bar that was installed in the wall. Cay heard the clink of glass against glass, and Morry reappeared bearing a squat glass of amber liquid and handed it to Cay. "*Bon Appétit.* I'll see you in the morning."

Cay lifted the glass to Morry in a salute, took a long swallow and was putting the glass down when the phone rang.

Morry stopped in the middle of the flight of stairs and gave a weary sigh.

"Go on to bed," Cay told him. "I'll get it."

Cay barely got the receiver to his ear when he heard a muffled voice say, "She's pretty, Sinclair, very pretty. Too bad she won't be that way when I get through with her."

2

"I DO NOT FIND HIM attractive."

The litany Toni intoned bounced off the walls of the bathroom. The house had been decorated as the ultimate love nest by Liz's friend of a friend, and the bathroom was frankly sensual. The walls were covered with velvety paper in the greens and blues of the ocean, and the sunken tub, made of aquamarine marble, was big enough to accommodate a table of four for bridge. "Good grief," Liz had exclaimed when she'd first seen it, "I'm afraid to get in. Jaws might be in there."

Jaws was not in the tub, just bubbles. Toni had tipped in half a bottle of frothy liquid before filling the tub. Stripped of her confining clothes and savoring the luxury of a quiet house and a warm bath to take away the lonelies, she'd climbed in and settled her bottom against the carved marble that had been artfully shaped to fit the human posterior.

The shelf behind her formed a seashell that fit her shoulders. She lay back, savoring the warmth and scent of the water.

Just as her muscles reached a lovely relaxed stage, the telephone began to ring. Diabolically insistent, its peals filled the house. Who could be calling her at this time of night? Sinclair? Telling her he'd changed his mind about their agreement? She snatched a towel from the rack, wrapped it around her body and ran down the stairs.

The phone stopped ringing when she got to the bottom step.

She returned to the bathroom, settled into the bubbles . . . and it began again.

Toni shook her head in exasperation . . . and let it ring. If it was Sinclair with the bad news that he'd changed his mind, she didn't want to hear it. Tomorrow was soon enough.

At the other end of the line, Cay Sinclair stood listening to the soft burr of the unanswered phone ringing in his ear. He gripped the receiver and muttered a soft curse. *Answer, Toni, dammit.* He knew she was there. He'd left her at the house himself. She had to be there.

He slammed the phone down and ran out the front door.

The telephone ringing stopped. Toni put her head back on the edge of the tub where it seemed to fit so nicely and let her mind drift into oblivion. Quiet, wonderful oblivion.

WHEN CAY SAW THE HOUSE blazing with lights, a chill shivered up his spine. He pounded on the door. She didn't come. He pounded again, harder this time, in the same fast rhythm his heart was beating. Still no answer . . . and the house was lit up like Times Square.

Agile as a child, he ran to the palm tree and swung himself up. The sturdy branch hanging over the balcony that he hadn't liked before was now a godsend. He edged his way out on it and dropped onto the floor of the second story porch, just outside a window.

From outside all he could see was a white filmy curtain. He tried the window. It was locked. But the next window was open to the night air; the screen was the only deterrent to his entry. The curtain billowed away, giving him a full view of the lighted room. It was a bedroom and empty at the moment. On the floor at the foot of the bed lay a puddle of black clothing. Toni was in the house ... somewhere. She'd ignored his telephone call. Had she done it because she hadn't heard it? Or because she hadn't wanted to hear it? Or, he thought with trepidation, was something terribly wrong?

He took out a penknife and, with great care and quiet, punctured the screen.

HOW MUCH LATER it was when the noise woke her, Toni couldn't guess. The sound didn't alarm her. It was probably a cat. There'd been one prowling around earlier—a sleek gray tom who thought two females would be a soft touch and was determined to adopt them. She listened, trying to identify the sound. Perhaps it was Liz returning home. But if it was Liz, why did the noises seem to be coming from the second-story balcony? Her relaxation vanished and her nerves tightened like violin strings. There was something in her bedroom.

Step. Pause. Step. Pause. A long silence.

Her heart was pounding. She sat up and considered the possibilities. Should she scream, cry out or stay very quiet? It would be hard to scream, especially since she couldn't breathe....

She knew she should get out of the tub, but it was already too late. The carpeting muffled the sound, but her supersensitive ears could hear footsteps coming closer.

Cay Sinclair leaned against the doorway of the bathroom, his mouth lifted in a cynical smile that kept her frightened heart beating at the same crazy pace.

Her fear blazed into a glorious burst of temper. "What do you think you're doing, walking in here and scaring me to death?"

His green eyes seemed to touch her skin. He was too engrossed in enjoying the sights to answer her. Damn him. He had her trapped.

"I came to see if you were entertaining any unwelcome guests."

"Not until just now."

How long had it been since he'd been in a woman's bathroom? He'd forgotten the rituals, the bubbles, the hair pinned up, the light feminine scent in the air. That she was angry heightened his sense of enjoyment. That she wore nothing but soap bubbles was even more intriguing.

"What unwelcome guest did you think I would be entertaining? Your feathered friend?" She looked up, way up, at the dark glossiness of his hair, which had the peculiar ability to trap every shred of light in the bathroom. She didn't like men with black hair sprinkled with strands of silver and beautiful green eyes that gleamed with an unholy light.

Sinclair watched her eyes flicker over him in that assessing, intelligent way of hers. The lady was much too smart for her own good. Exactly how smart was she? Smart enough to aid and abet Torgen in extortion? Cay decided it might be in his own best interests to stay right where he was and find out. *Dreadful task you've given yourself, Sinclair.*

He knelt down next to the tub.

She stared back at him, her gray eyes wide. She looked vulnerable . . . and beautiful. Was she a lovely liar as well?

Carefully avoiding the pink warm curves, which he couldn't quite see below the water, he reached out and touched a bubble that floated in front of her. It didn't pop. It adhered to his finger.

Toni watched, thinking that even soap bubbles weren't immune to his charm. It was hard for her to be dignified when a self-assured male was kneeling beside her dabbling in the soap bubbles that floated next to her naked body, but Toni gave it a Herculean try. "I'd like you to leave."

He brought the captive bubble up and placed it with infinite care on the bridge of her nose. The feather-light touch of his finger teased as it left her warm, wet skin. "Would you?"

She glared at him, like an owl whose feathers had been ruffled. "Yes."

Another bubble was carefully deposited next to the first, closer to the tip of her nose.

"Don't—" she was talking through a tight throat now"—do this. I don't know you."

"We'll get acquainted. You start. Tell me where you met Torgén."

She felt a heat that didn't come from the bathwater. "I told you, I've never seen the man in my life before tonight."

"Are you sure?" With infinite care, he brought a cluster of bubbles up to perch on her shoulder. He leaned back to examine the arrangement, and as if the aesthetic effect wasn't quite what he was seeking, he set about to improve it with another cluster of bubbles.

A lean fingertip as smooth as drawn silk, as gentle as the flick of a cat's tail circled her shoulder with a practiced surety that lifted the fine hairs at the nape of her neck. Her mind and body battled each other for supremacy.

"I'm quite . . . sure I don't know him."

"I'm glad to hear that."

He said the words so lightly, so carefully, that she was sure he didn't mean them. "Would you please—"

"Please what?" He brought another cluster of bubbles up and deposited them in the soft hollow of her throat, coaxing them to adhere to her wet skin with a concentration that made her breath catch. He dipped into the water again, and this time his hand lingered perilously close to the rosy tip that was hidden under the surface. She lay where she was, unable to move. The bubbles he'd painted her with began a slow descent into the valley between her breasts.

He reached out a finger to block them. Clamoring nerves fed a message to her brain: *Run.* "Sinclair—"

"Your skin is like satin. . . ."

This can't be happening to me. Mike walked out of the apartment exactly ten days ago. I can't be feeling like this, not again, not so soon. . . .

She looked so exquisitely distressed, so utterly adorable. He needed to touch her badly, and so he did the least threatening thing he could think of; he reached under the water, found her hand and brought it up to press his mouth to the back of it.

The tingles gathered, coalesced, exploded. "Don't . . . play the chivalrous knight with me." Nothing seemed to be working right, especially her voice.

"Would you like something more modern?" He turned her hand and flicked his tongue over her palm.

Her reaction was automatic. Jerking her hand, she squeezed her wet fingers together and tried to slither out of his hard grip. Her other hand came up to join in the battle. He relaxed his hold, but when she thought victory was hers, he shackled both her hands and held them in front of her as if she were his captive.

Water ran in tiny rivulets from her wet hands over his. "Toni, my sweet," he said in an even tone that wasn't reflected by the dark look in his eyes, "I don't want to be uncomplimentary, but you're turning into a prune. Do you suppose I could ask you to get out of that marble monstrosity and get some clothes on so we could talk?"

She moved restlessly in the water, fighting the urge to splash and soak him from head to heel. His eyes warned her not to. "We have nothing to talk about."

"I'm afraid we do. Unless—" a dark brow lifted mockingly "—you'd like to conduct our discussion in here? It certainly looks as if there's room enough for two."

A sudden vision of Cay Sinclair sliding into the tub with her, his body as bare as hers, flashed into her head. It was the stuff of dreams—dreams that mocked and taunted her, dreams that couldn't come true. "You wouldn't want to walk around smelling of lilacs, would you?"

"I've never tried it, but who knows? I might like it. We'd match." He got to his feet, steeling himself to take in the sight of warm, pink feminine curves hiding under the frothy mound of bubbles. "Don't be long, will you?" He turned and strolled out of the room, leaving her to stare after him in dazed wonder.

Cay thought she might keep him waiting—but it wasn't very much later that she came down the stairs swathed from throat to ankles in a white terry robe. Her feet were bare.

She moved around the living room and looked adorable, clutching the collar of her robe and trying to play the perfect hostess. She asked him if he'd like something to drink and when he shook his head, thinking that he was going to need his wits about him for the rest of this night, she looked vaguely distressed.

"Usually at this time of night I go out on the patio and sit and think about how cold it is up north and how glad I am that I'm not there. Would you like to join me?"

He was amused. She obviously didn't want to be with him in this plush room with its velvet sofas and a picture of a reclining nude above the fireplace. He glanced up at the picture, then back at Toni and ordered himself sternly to forget that there were curves under the terry robe that surpassed those of the woman in that idealized painting for silkiness and feminine appeal. "I'd rather stay here, if you don't mind." He settled into the couch that faced the painting and kept his eyes on Toni. Smiling faintly, he watched her choose the chair with its back turned to the portrait.

"In case you're wondering who she is," Toni said, glancing at the painting, "I can't tell you. We're house sitting for a friend of a friend of Liz's."

He let her think he was interested in the portrait, giving himself a minute to let his mind work. He could see why someone had offered the place to Liz and Toni rent free. It was much better to have a house like this occupied than left vacant. While she'd been dressing, he'd done a little checking. The place was about as easy to secure as those soap bubbles he'd found her in a moment before. He'd propped a stick in the frame of a back window to stop any intruder from prying it open, but he still didn't think the house was burglarproof—or Torgen proof.

She tucked a leg up under herself and caught his eyes with hers. Launching soldierlike into the fray, she said, "As a cat burglar, you're a dismal failure. Would you like to explain why you came swinging in my window tonight like Tarzan?"

He could feel a smile start at the corner of his mouth. "Why do you think I did?"

"I have no idea. Why don't you enlighten me?"

He hesitated, not understanding his quixotic urge to shield her from the unpleasant truth. But perhaps she already knew the unpleasant truth. She might have planned everything down to the last detail . . . including his reluctance to suspect her. "When I returned home, I received a telephone call."

"I'm sure that's not an earthshaking occurrence. You must get many calls—"

"Not like this one."

"How was it . . . different?"

"It was a threat. Directed at you."

A silence hung in the room between them. She seemed very still. The only sign that she was nervous was the minute stroke of her fingers over the fold of terry cloth she'd tugged over her knee. "Don't be absurd. I have no money. The only think of value that I own is my equipment, and I don't even own that. The bank does."

She had shrugged off the threat to her life quickly. Too quickly? Because she knew it wasn't genuine? She'd also been frank about her financial status. Too frank? Was she trying to disarm him by appearing candid? "The caller thinks you mean something to me."

He watched her like an interrogator with a suspect, but if she was an actress, she was a damn good one. Disbelief flashed over her face, followed by comprehension.

As if she could no longer sit still, she unfolded her legs and walked to a window to stare out into the street. He looked at her white terry-clad back and wondered if she had moved away to keep him from seeing the expression of triumph on her face.

God, but it felt wrong to be thinking thoughts like that about a slim woman who stood hugging herself as if she were fighting fear. Her back was so straight. Too straight. She looked so alone.

Still standing there by the window, staring out at something he couldn't see, she said, "You were only a voice on the telephone to me before tonight."

Her cool, quiet words seemed to enter his bloodstream. She turned around slowly, and a tiny shock went through him. Without makeup, looking like a child braced for a lecture, she was more tantalizingly familiar than ever. A memory too far away, too vague to remember teased at his brain.

With a start, he realized she was saying something to him.

". . . think your caller was that man we met tonight?"

He forced himself to look relaxed, but he didn't feel relaxed. He didn't like being so damn unsure of her. Was she, as was everyone else, determined to get a little something from a man who, according to the press, had so much money that he couldn't spend it all in a lifetime? Or was she exactly what she appeared to be—a loner who'd just lost her lover and wasn't feeling especially charitable toward the world in general and men in particular. If . . . No, he couldn't start empathizing with her. He'd learned long before what schemers women are. What chance was there that she was sincere? Probably none. "Possibly it was. I have no way of knowing for sure."

"Are you going to tell me what he has against you?"

He tilted his head back to study her and said lazily, "I thought perhaps you already knew."

Suddenly she no longer looked like a child. She looked like a woman well used to facing off with men. "The last time I had a friend who wore feathers I was ten years old and she was a chicken whose name was Henny Penny."

Cay fought back the urge to smile at the thought of a ten-year-old girl with a chicken tucked under her arm and forced himself to continue down the track he'd started on—the track he'd been on since the moment he'd swung down from that palm tree and discovered she hadn't answered his call. "He's threatened to make you . . . a little less attractive." She blanched in such an evident reaction of fear that his conscience went into high gear, screaming at him to let her alone. All the pushing and probing and touching lightly with rapier-like questions felt . . . wrong.

"He has a real piquant sense of humor, doesn't he?" He hated hearing the tone that came into her voice, a self-mocking bravado that shut him out and left her alone in that lonely cubicle of life she seemed quite used to inhabiting. "Can we go to the police?"

She sounded as if she meant it. Or was it simply that he wanted to believe her? And Cay did. Some part of him that had been buried for years wanted desperately to believe her. "Not at this point—not when he hasn't actually done anything."

"He's done something. He's scared me out of my mind."

"Has he?" he asked blandly, watching her.

Had he thought she was short? She seemed to grow inches before his eyes from sheer will. "This is a totally nonproductive conversation." She was as cool as an ice floe. "I suggest we end it. We can talk in the morning if you like. I spent most of the day driving and I'm very tired. I'd like to go to bed."

"I'm going with you."

Her shock was real. So was the way she was controlling herself. Her eyes flashed a hot, clear, go-to-hell message, but the words that came out of her mouth were frosty with control. "Mr. Sinclair, I don't know what . . . extracurricular privileges you imagine your position as producer gives you, but let me assure you that this trip out, at least, it does not give you carte blanche with the hired help!"

"That bedroom of yours is an open invitation to anybody who wants to come in," he clarified.

She let her eyes travel over him. "Yes, isn't it?"

"I was only thinking of your safety."

"How considerate of you." If the house hadn't already been air-conditioned, the tone of her voice would have cooled him well enough.

Toni watched his eyes moving over the fur rugs, the fringed lamps, the grandiose white china cats with their long necks, the black Oriental furniture, the velvet couch. The room exuded opulence, comfort, sensual indulgence. His visual tour ended with the couch arm under his fingers. She thought she'd made it clear this place wasn't her idea of House Beautiful. He couldn't think the sensuality in the room had anything to do with her. *Could he?* "Does this thing make up into a bed?"

"Yes."

Looking like a man with a purpose, he picked up the lacquered coffee table and placed it to one side out of the way.

He might be her boss, but he couldn't be under the impression that she'd allow him to stay the night after one meal together. "Wait a minute. What do you think you're doing?"

He began to grope under the couch for the handle. "Where are the pullouts for this thing?"

"Two, one on each side. Listen to me, you can't—"

He stopped in the act of lifting the bed out. "You've used it before?"

"How on earth could I? I just arrived in Key West today. I know about couch beds. I slept on one most of my life. If there isn't a handle in the middle, there's always one on each side. Now that I've given you an extended course in the care and feeding of couch beds, would you please go?"

"You're right. There are two handles." He lifted and tugged and the bed appeared. Sheets had been neatly laid on the mammoth mattress. They were green satin, bright as an emerald . . . and the exact color of his eyes.

Over the shimmering material, his twinkling gaze met hers. "I'm surprised there wasn't a button to push. Everything else seems so . . . convenient."

Had she thought he was too deadly serious? She would have traded his sober face of a moment ago for the devils of amusement that lurked in his eyes now. The panic she'd felt the second he walked in the bathroom struck again...with redoubled strength. "Liz will be home any minute."

"Fine. We can be quite comfortable here until she arrives."

"We are not going to be comfortable anywhere. *We* are going home."

Her cutting use of the royal we didn't seem to bother him at all. He merely looked thoughtful. "Perhaps that is a better idea."

She sighed in exasperation. "The joke is over. Get out of here, Sinclair."

"No, I don't think so."

Her fear went up the scale five more notches. She couldn't afford to antagonize him, but she couldn't afford to let him stay. He was far too danger- ous...too...too something. She wasn't sure what. But what was she going to do? She needed to stay on civil terms with him, at least, until the next two concerts were over. Whether he would still want her to work on his show after the accusations he'd made was a ques- tion she didn't want to think about. She'd already mentally spent the two hundred and fifty dollars he'd offered her a dozen times over.

Somehow, this impasse had to be resolved with grace and dignity. "You don't have to stay for my protec- tion."

"Maybe I'm staying for mine."

"What exactly does that mean?"

"It means that I'm curious about what you're up to, and the only way I can discover whether you're wait- ing to hear from our feathered friend is to stay with you the rest of the night. On the other hand, if you're tell- ing me the truth about not knowing him, and he means what he says . . . then that's all the more reason I should stay."

This was the crowning touch. If she insisted he leave now, he would suspect her all the more. But to have him stay would open the door to other thoughts—forbid- den, not-to-be-dreamed thoughts.

He didn't trust her and, strangely enough, that hurt. It was logical for him to feel that way; after all, he hardly knew her. But it still hurt.

She couldn't protest again against him staying the night and let him think he was right to suspect her. If he wanted to stay, she'd let him . . . as long as he was downstairs, a flight away. All she had to do was walk up the stairs, shut the door and prop a chair under the knob.

Her quick look toward the staircase betrayed her intentions.

"You take one step toward those stairs and you'll find yourself flat on this bed with me on top of you like a paperweight." His dark velvety voice had a steel core. "If you don't want that to happen, you'd better just slip out of that robe and get under the sheet."

"I don't have a nightgown on."

"Too bad." His drawl mocked softly.

She let the succinct words and the message they carried pass by. "I'll just go upstairs and get one—"

He was around the couch and shackling her wrist before she had taken the second step. "You don't need one."

She'd thought her reaction to him when he'd touched her in the bathtub had been bad, but this was much worse. He was standing so close that instinct told her he would sense the slightest yielding on her part instantly. The sensitive agile hand wrapped around her wrist seemed to be taking her pulse. And if it was, he'd know exactly how much he disturbed her. But if he felt anything at the contact of his fingers on her wrist, it didn't show in his face.

Cay held her, wondering what in God's name he would do if she took him up on his threat. The last thing in the world he wanted to do was throw this woman down on the bed and escalate the war between them. Under his fingers, her skin felt as silky as a child's, and her pulse pounded in a syncopated beat that roughly matched his own. Idly he noticed a strand of hair clinging to her ear. She wore her hair short, but now when it was drying, it had a tendency to curl up at the ends. She looked so fragile, so vulnerable, that he wanted to pull her close and kiss her.

The look on her face betrayed her deep dislike for him. He didn't blame her. At this moment, he didn't much like himself. He'd never manhandled a woman in his life. He'd never had to, he thought derisively. They'd all been more than willing....

He relaxed his hold on her, but his voice was gruff as he spoke. "You misunderstand me. I meant that you could sleep in your robe."

"Let go of me."

"I've got to go up and secure that window. I can only hope I don't find someone up there waiting for me. Now, shall I take you along, or will you stay here and wait for me?"

"I'll wait here," she said coolly.

He could see that she disliked him intensely, but her animosity didn't keep him from admiring the softness of her flushed cheeks, the curling tendrils of her velvet-black hair. "A wise choice."

TONI STOOD on the other side of the bed, putting its wide expanse between herself and the stairs, waiting, breath held. The house was silent. Too silent. She should be able to hear him walking around upstairs. Why couldn't she? That window had been left open. If Cay Sinclair could get in easily, what would stop someone more unscrupulous from entering the house the same way and lying in wait for him?

Why should she care?

She did care. When his jeaned legs reappeared on the stairs, relief rushed through her. Quickly rearranging her face to hide her feelings, she said, "I suppose it's . . . safe for me to go up now?"

"You're not going anywhere."

The antique fringed lamp filled the room with golden shadows, enclosing shadows. The bed was covered with satin sheets, and Cay stood on the other side of it, looking dark, masculine and utterly determined. The soft light accented his cheekbones, made a shadow at the hollow of his throat and concealed the expression in his eyes. Primitive power and controlled strength coexisted inside his muscled frame—a power that reached out to her, a strength that held back.

"I take it you expect me to climb into bed with you."

He never wavered. "No. You can sleep in the chair if you like."

Moving as lithely as a cat, he sat down on the side of the bed and began to pull off his shoes. His wide shoulders strained the thin cloth of his shirt as his well-developed muscles moved in smooth coordination.

"Your chivalry only extends to kisses on the hand, I see."

He stood up and unbuttoned his shirt, each movement of his hands and wrists as graceful and as smooth as they were on the keyboard of a piano. "There isn't a reason in the world we can't share the same bed for one night," he said in a bland tone, his eyes as cool and knowing as they'd been the first time she saw him. "You say you're tired; so am I." His hands went to the buckle of his belt, and he unfastened it as casually as if he made his living shedding his clothes on stage rather than playing music.

Instantly furious, she swung away... and found herself facing the nude portrait. The woman lay on a red velvet couch, a filmy veil over her seductively turned hips, the smile on her mouth aimed like an arrow at Toni.

The light went out, turning the room a shadowy, mysterious gray. Behind her, slippery satin seemed to whisper. Cay Sinclair was climbing into bed.

"I thought only horses could sleep standing up."

She turned around, pulled back the sheet and slid into the bed, every nerve on edge. Behind her closed lids, the vision of the dark form on the other side of the bed lingered... while her ears picked up the soft sound of a masculine laugh.

Toni wasn't exactly sure when she began to time his breathing. It seemed as if she'd been lying there for hours, holding her arms stiffly to her sides. She wasn't a curler; she was a sprawler. She'd been that way since she left home. Finally sleeping alone, after years of crowded quarters shared with three sisters, she'd wallowed in the luxury of having a bed to herself, and now sprawling was a habit.

That was why she was afraid to relax and go to sleep. She couldn't risk letting her hands stray from her body.

THERE WAS A STRANGE WARMTH in the region of her elbow. Toni opened her eyes... and discovered her worst fears were realized. She had rolled over on her stomach and her bent elbow was an inch from his face.

She couldn't fault Cay. He'd kept his promise. She was the trespasser encroaching on his space. On the other side of her, there was an ocean of green satin big enough for three people. Crawling back across that space and sliding out of bed without waking him was going to be impossible.

Morning light streamed in the window, filtering tentatively across Cay's face. He slept turned toward her on his side, his breathing deep and even. Even asleep, he was darkly appealing. The deep-set hollow of his eyes was set off by straight black brows that didn't quite match and by equally black curved lashes. His mouth had a sultry relaxed droop, and he was deeply tanned everywhere she could see—his cheeks, his throat, his bronzed bare shoulder. He had the sheet wrapped under his arm like a toga, and the contrast of green satin and copper skin was . . . unthinkable. These thoughts were totally unthinkable.

Carefully, holding her breath, she moved her elbow away from his nose and tucked her arm under her. Two rolls brought her to the side of the bed. On her feet, she tugged at her loosened robe, wrapping the tie around her waist. It was a good thing she'd awakened first.

He made a sound, a sleepy groan. Her eyes flew to his face, but he didn't stir. Afraid to breathe, she crept across the living room on bare feet and climbed the stairs. Her last glimpse of him showed him deep in sleep.

Standing under a tepid shower, she ran a washcloth over her shoulder . . . and remembered the touch of a teasing finger. She reached up to turn off the water, and the spray poured over the wrist he had held. How insane this all was. She'd played with Mike, touched him . . . loved him. But at the moment, she couldn't recall a second of it—not with the intensity she remembered two casual encounters with Cay Sinclair.

Annoyed, she pawed through her suitcase, which she hadn't had a chance to unpack, and found a pair of ragged cutoffs and a turquoise gauze top that would keep her cool. When she was dressed, she ran a comb through her dark hair, trying to tame the turned up ends. Hopeless.

She crept down the stairs only to find that Cay Sinclair was no longer in bed. The couch was neatly made up and the pillows propped on the back of it. She followed her nose to the kitchen and found Cay and Liz sitting together at the table drinking coffee and looking as if they were a committee of two that met regularly at this time of day.

Liz looked delighted. What did she have to be so happy about? Toni's eyes flashed her a message. *Some friend. Where were you when I needed you?*

Toni poured herself some coffee, but didn't come to the table. Wasn't there an old saying that warned one against taking sustenance with the enemy? She leaned back against the counter.

"Sleep well?" he asked in a bland tone.

"Very. And yourself?"

"I didn't fare quite as well as you did. Amazing how someone who takes up so little space when she's on her feet turns out to be an octopus in bed."

A muffled sound escaped Liz, a choked gasp of laughter.

"The worst of it was," Cay went on in the same calm tone, having been given entirely too much encouragement by Liz's laugh, "every time I tried to get you to move over, you poked your elbow at me."

Heat rose in Toni's face, but she stayed where she was and looked Cay Sinclair in the eye. "In my family, we slept four in a bed, and you only kept as much territory as you could defend."

"I've heard of battles in the bedroom, but this adds a whole new dimension to the problem."

Liz chortled and Sinclair's mouth had a look of controlled amusement that Toni was beginning to recognize. Toni wondered if Sinclair was now ready to believe she'd told him the truth as there had been no further word from the man with the feathers. The air around him had certainly thawed. He seemed more relaxed, and his primitive appeal was heightened by the morning stubble he wore.

"I'm glad I'm contributing to your education."

Cay watched Toni tilt her upturned nose a fraction of an inch higher. He'd given Liz her instructions, and he hoped to hell she'd follow them. He was ninety-nine percent sure that Liz was telling him the truth— that she knew nothing of Torgen and that neither did Toni. Because he trusted Liz, he'd enlisted her cooperation to help him see that Toni remained unharmed. "I'd love to stay and continue this interesting tour into higher learning, but I must go." He looked at Liz and added softly, "I'm counting on you."

"No problem. Everything's under control."

He stood up, said goodbye and walked out of the kitchen, taking his leave as easily as if he were walking off the stage after a successful performance. Liz didn't get up to see him out. Her gaze sought Toni's face.

Toni averted her eyes from Liz's and stood unmoving, her hands wrapped around her coffee cup. The sound of the door opening and closing shivered across her nerves. He was gone and she was glad . . . but why did the house seem empty of life?

Worse, why did she feel she could no longer trust Liz? She'd known her for three years and they'd shared so much. They'd eaten peanut butter sandwiches when times were bad and lobster when times were good. They'd gone walking in the rain when they couldn't afford to ride. But now the silence in the kitchen seemed to stretch into a barrier she couldn't break.

At last, she lifted her head, sought out Liz's eyes with hers and asked, "What was that little exchange all about?"

"What little exchange?" Liz countered, her voice careful.

"You know which one. 'I'm counting on you,'" Toni said in a low voice, poorly imitating Cay. Then, in a falsetto that vaguely resembled Liz's voice, she said, "'No problem. Everything's under control.'"

"We're going to take care of you. Watch you round the clock."

"I don't need watching," she said slowly, distinctly, as if she were talking to a child, "I can take care of myself."

"I've got the day shift and Cay's taking nights."

"Over my dead body," Toni murmured feelingly.

Liz went on as if she hadn't heard. "He wants it that way." Liz tilted her head and Toni braced herself. "I didn't know that couch was hiding a set of green satin sheets."

Toni made a face. "Neither did I."

"Was that the reason you two didn't use your bedroom?"

"Whatever you're thinking...stop thinking it. Nothing happened between Cay Sinclair and me."

Liz's eyes widened. "Nothing happened? Oh, come on, Toni. It's all right. You can tell me the truth."

"I'm not lying. We slept in the same bed, but we didn't—"

"Is *make love* the phrase you're grouping for?"

"Groping," Toni corrected.

"You mean you really didn't make love with that gorgeous hunk of a man?"

Toni sighed with exasperation. "No, I really didn't."

"That's prophetic," Liz said disgustedly.

She had Toni's attention now. "Prophetic? What do you mean?"

"You know. Sad."

"You mean pathetic."

"That, too. But that makes it all the more romantic. He must be falling in love with you."

"Exactly how did you arrive at that conclusion?"

"If he didn't make love with you, but he still wants to look out for you, what other explanation can there be?"

"There are probably a dozen or so, but I'm sure you wouldn't want to hear them. Liz, listen—" she set her cup down on the counter "—he doesn't trust me. He thinks I'm in on some scheme with this guy I don't even know."

"Well, maybe he does, but he's still not willing to take any chances with your life. Somebody's going to be with you every moment from now on."

"Terrific," Toni murmured, her eyes playing over Liz's face.

Liz looked down at her cup. "Look, I don't want anything to happen to you. You're my friend. I haven't had many in my lifetime . . . and you're one of the best I've ever had. I don't want to lose you."

Contrite, Toni walked to the table, sat down by Liz and put her hand over the other woman's. "I'll do my best to stay healthy."

3

LATER THAT DAY, while Liz and Toni were at the beach, lying on sand the color of bleached bones, improving their tans, Toni closed her eyes to the sun and thought about Cay Sinclair's bargain with Liz. Was he really concerned about her? Or was this another ploy of his?

Cay Sinclair had enlisted Liz to act as a guard dog, and then he'd disappeared into the morning air, leaving Liz to tell Toni that they'd set up a surveillance schedule worthy of the crown jewels. She wondered if he'd even instructed Liz on the approach to use, telling her to play on Toni's loyalty. No, he couldn't have. Cay Sinclair didn't know her that well. Actually, he didn't know her at all. And he trusted her even less.

But he trusted Liz on sight. Why doesn't he trust you?
Because that man in the street called you by name.

That wasn't so strange. She wasn't shy about putting her name around; she made her living by being known for what she did. And it wasn't any secret that she was doing the sound for three of the festival's concerts. Her name had appeared in the publicity releases here in Key West when she'd signed the contract a month ago, and anyone interested in such things would have read about it.

The thought made her restless. She sat up and stared out over the ocean, gazing at the calm, still water that was as green as Sinclair's eyes....

Toni curled her arms around her legs defensively and pulled into herself. Sparkles rebounded into her eyes from light caught on the surface of the water. The ocean was unpredictable and often treacherous...like men— like Cay Sinclair's friend.

Who was he?

Her fingers dropped to the sand and touched a clam shell. It was smooth, cool . . . and as noncommittal as Sinclair had been. She hadn't learned a thing from him last night.

She couldn't go on pretending she wasn't interested. She had to know what was going on. What she needed was an efficient private eye or somebody with a nose for news, somebody who knew something about Sinclair's friends.

Suddenly, the tension fell away. She would take action, do something. A surge of joy made it difficult for her to lie passively in the sun. "I'm going for a swim," she told the reclining figure next to her.

Liz's eyes came wide open. She stared at Toni, as if she couldn't remember where she was. "I'm going with you."

"You're not even awake. Go back to sleep."

"The water will wake me up." Liz pushed herself into a sitting position.

Toni watched her, wondering what Sinclair had said to infuse Liz with such enthusiasm for guarding her. If he were any other man, she'd have marched to his house and told him to mind his own business. But she couldn't risk offending him. She was responsible for Liz's livelihood as well as her own, and whether she liked it or not, she couldn't afford to antagonize him. On the other hand, she wouldn't let him run her life. When she saw Sinclair tonight, she'd tell him that this business of watching her as if she were the president-elect had to stop. But first, she'd place that call to Miami. . . .

"WHEN ARE YOU LEAVING?" Morry slouched in the white wicker chair across the patio table from Cay.

"In about an hour or so, I suppose. I told Liz I'd be there by six."

The two men had finished their evening meal and were sitting in the garden behind the house, relaxing over a glass of iced tea. The lawn around them was a plush green carpet. Above them, a white table umbrella shielded them from the last rays of the afternoon sun.

Cay leaned back, savoring the cool peace of his favorite sanctuary. The birds and bees were quiet at this time of day. The only sound was the splashing of water, coming from the fountain he'd had installed a few years ago. A young nymph tipped her jug of water and the shimmering liquid fell perpetually into the marble basin below, joggling the green leaves of the water lilies floating on the surface.

He'd had the fountain put in three years ago, when he spent his first year in Key West, and he'd never regretted giving himself this one small indulgence. He sat watching it, the sound of the dripping water soothing his nerves.

"How did Torgen find out you were in Key West? He's never tracked you down here before."

The peace he'd felt a moment ago was shattered. Cay didn't want to think about Toni and the fact she might be wrapped up with Torgen. He'd been very carefully avoiding the thought all day, even though he'd been conscious that tonight he was going to see her again. He drummed his fingers on the glass tabletop in a syncopated rhythm. "I suppose my presence here isn't exactly a secret."

He wasn't looking at Morry, but he could sense his old friend's edginess.

"There was one local press release a month ago. The only people who knew before that were the members of the Key West Association. That august group consists of five very rich women and two very rich men. Not a group of people Torgen would be likely to rub elbows with."

"What are you trying to say, Morry?"

"What about that woman you spent the night with? What proof have you got that she can be trusted?"

"As much as any human being has about another he's met for the first time," he said, his tone casual. Cay didn't understand his state of mind. He'd asked himself the same question throughout the day, but for some reason, he didn't want to hear Morry's suspicions about Toni. "The chances are good that she's harmless."

"Don't be too sure. She might be in on it."

"What makes you think so?" He wanted to hear Morry's reasoning. Maybe his own didn't make any sense. Maybe Morry's didn't, either, and hearing it would help him see the holes in it.

"This whole thing smells like a set up from start to finish. Torgen accosts you on the street. Then he threatens the lady. You rush in to act the chivalrous knight and stand guard duty. Bingo. You're hooked. You volunteer to stay with her at night, and she plies you with her charms. Maybe not too obviously. Maybe she gives you the hands-off treatment first, just to make sure you don't suspect anything. Then, when she's led you down the garden path, she hits you for money."

"You should write fiction."

Morry's eyes narrowed. "You should have your head examined if you fall for this scam."

"I've considered the possibility that she's a decoy. Especially since Torgen seemed to know her. He called her by name when he approached us last night."

Morry leaned forward and looked as if he'd discovered gold. "That clinches it, then. I did some checking on her this afternoon. She's in debt, boss. Two thousand dollars on that equipment."

"She mentioned that casually in passing."

"She mentioned a two-thousand-dollar debt casually in passing? Why would she do that unless she's setting things up so it will be easier for you to understand her need for money when she makes her final pitch? Come on, Cay. Fire her. Get her out of Key West . . . and out of your life."

"I can't fire her. She's got a contract."

"Oh, hell, call Malcolm. He can find a loophole in it big enough to drive a truck through. That's his speciality. Have him get rid of her."

"Not . . . just . . . yet."

"Not just yet?" Morry was incredulous. "Why? Because she's cute? You wouldn't be the first guy to fall for an innocent face that hid a mind like Machiavelli's."

"I haven't fallen for an innocent face in ten years," Sinclair drawled.

"Maybe it comes in ten-year cycles."

"Thanks. There's a couple of things that bother me, though. If she is in cahoots with Torgen, why would he give the game away the first night out? And, when I offered her money to do the sound for my concert, she refused to take five hundred. She's doing it for two-fifty."

Morry's eyes bored into him. "So, for two hundred and fifty dollars, she bought your trust. Cheap at half the price. And damn clever of her."

"My trust isn't something you can buy, Morry. You ought to know that by now."

"MIAMI SUN TIMES."

The feeling that she was doing something wrong pervaded Toni's entire being. Having been brought up in close quarters with seven siblings, she'd been taught that snooping was a cardinal sin that ranked right up there next to lying. But she'd been waiting ever since they'd gotten home from the beach for Liz to go upstairs and get ready for her evening out with Tommy, and she couldn't lose the precious opportunity she had for privacy. Still in the bikini she'd worn at the beach, Toni clutched the receiver and said, "I would like to speak to Harold Ferguson."

"Mr. Ferguson isn't in right now. I'll try to page him and have him return your call."

Toni glanced at the kitchen clock, feeling as if, caught in the act of sinning, she was being punished. *Stop being so paranoid.* Of course he wasn't there at fifteen minutes to five in the afternoon. Pop music critics weren't expected to be in their offices regular hours, and she knew that. She should have checked the time before she dialed. "Thank you." She gave the woman her name and number and hung up.

Now she was stuck. She'd have to stay downstairs and wait for the call. She wouldn't be able to go up and change. Luckily, when the phone rang an hour later, Liz still hadn't come downstairs, and she could talk with relative ease.

"Where in hell are you, Pereola?"

"Hello, Fergy," she said pleasantly, beating down the clamoring voice of her conscience. It didn't feel right to call him just because she needed information. She'd gone out with him a few times, and he'd seemed nice enough—until she met Mike. Fergy had taken his fall from grace philosophically. "Nice to hear your voice. I'm calling because I need some information. I wondered if you could tell me something about—"

"Uh-uh. Nothing doing. Not till you tell me where you are."

She hesitated and then said, "I'm in Key West, working. Some of us do work for a living, you know."

It was a familiar jibe. Ferguson ignored it. "Who are you doing sound for?"

"It's a series of concerts, a package deal. Listen, do you know anything about a friend of Cay Sinclair's who isn't particularly friendly and runs around in weird costumes?"

There was a silence, then a chuckle. "Sinclair's not that kind of guy, Toni."

A wry smile lifted her lips. "I know he's not. But—"

"Can't you give me something a little more concrete . . . like a name?"

"I don't know his name. All I know is that he dresses like one of the Three Musketeers, feathers on the hat and all."

There was a silence on the line while Fergy thought. He had a close to photographic memory, and Toni knew that if he had any knowledge at all inside his brain about Cay's friend, he'd come up with it. "Doesn't ring any bells, Toni. Sorry."

"I'm sorry, too," she said thoughtfully, feeling disappointed. She'd been so sure he'd be able to tell her what she needed to know. Fergy kept track of the personalities in the music world, and he had a fetish for Sinclair. He thought Sinclair's music was both intelligent and wildly emotional. He'd written once that Sinclair had the ultimate intellect, a mind able to combine rock, jazz and classical elements into a tasty stew that was creative, original and mind-blowing.

"So Sinclair's down there with you."

Ferguson's favorite reporter's ploy was to ask a question that sounded like a statement of fact.

With the deftness she had learned the hard way in the last three years, Toni neither confirmed nor denied it. "If you think of anything, will you call me?"

"Is Sinclair's friend harassing him or you?"

Had she thought she could deal with Fergy's agile brain? What a mistake. "I haven't said—"

"Oh, come on, Toni. You can't call me up and ask a question like that and not expect a few in return."

"You can ask, but I'm not answering. If you remember anything about this friend—"

"Wait a minute. Feathers. Crazy costumes. What does this Count of Monte Cristo look like?"

"He's short, dark-haired, I think, and he's got a narrow chin."

"That's him, it's got to be. The period getup threw me off. He was into Moroccan djellabas when I last saw him."

"Moroccan djellabas?"

"Desert cloaks. I'll bet your mystery man is Torgen, his old drummer. Especially if he's harassing Sinclair. A year after he retired, Sinclair was involved in some kind of court case with this nut. What was his first name? Something biblical, some handle his revival-preacher father gave him. Adam? No, not Adam. Jeremiah—Jeremiah Torgen. Nobody uses his first name now. Torgen would kill them if they did."

"What was the court case about?"

"When Sinclair quit giving concerts, he agreed to give Torgen an amount of money out of his future earnings. Torgen was taking him to court to get the percentage increased. The court case got some press coverage because of Sinclair's involvement... and Torgen's outlandish costumes."

"Did Torgen win?"

"Naw. Under that robe, Torgen didn't have a leg to stand on. He lost the case and had to pay the court fees besides. It was a mess, one old friend betraying another for filthy lucre. There was a woman involved, too, if I remember correctly."

"Involved—how?"

"How is a woman usually involved?" Ferguson said dryly. "Both men wanted her. Now, I've answered your question, how about you answering mine? Is Sinclair in Key West?"

"This is out of your territory, Fergy."

"But close enough to arouse my prurient interest. Come on, honey. Give."

"And be found guilty of contributing to the delinquency of a minor?"

He snorted. They were exactly the same age, their birthdays one day apart, hers on the day earlier. "You're lucky if I don't come right through the phone at you. Listen, Toni, be careful, will you? Sinclair is not known for his restraint with women."

"Maybe his publicity has been overdone."

"And maybe it hasn't. You have a care, Toni. You're a cheeky, disrespectful brat, but as brats go, you're okay. Stay away from Sinclair's bed and stay out of trouble. Reinforce his sound...not his ego. I don't want you to get hurt."

"Thanks for the warning. I'll be careful; you can count on it."

As Toni hung up the phone, she heard a step on the tiled floor behind her, a step that wasn't Liz's. She braced herself and turned around.

Sinclair stood leaning against the door, his hands full of red roses wrapped in green paper, his assessing gaze running over her nearly nude body. His eyes were dark, cynical and knowing.

He'd heard what she'd said...and had placed the worst possible interpretation on it.

"I didn't hear you come in." She wished her heart would stop pounding. She felt as if her chest would burst. What a fool she was. If Sinclair had entertained any doubts about her honesty, she'd certainly reinforced them. "The flowers are beautiful."

"They were a way of saying I was sorry." He took a step toward her and tossed them on the counter beside her as if they were so much excess baggage he wanted to rid himself of. A petal from one of the roses didn't survive the jarring and fluttered to the floor, a velvety casualty of his controlled anger. He said, "Your telephone conversation must have been very...important to distract you so thoroughly."

She picked up the petal from the floor, then turned her back to him and busied herself looking through the cupboards for a vase and then with unwrapping the roses with tender care that she hoped would somehow undo the damage he'd done to them a moment before. When she'd finished with the flowers and set the vase in the middle of the table, she faced him, her eyes direct and cool. "It was. Would you like some coffee?"

"To dilute my suspicions?"

This was war at its most refined, fought Sinclair style, the rapier thrust so quick and true that the swordsman knows he's scored before he delivers the blow.

Toni braced herself against the counter and faced him, determined not to be overwhelmed by the sensual appeal of his mocking smile and lithe body. "If I'm going to be accused of conspiring against you, I at least have the right to know who it is I'm supposed to be conspiring with."

He made no sign that he either agreed or disagreed with her. "No one has accused you of anything."

"Yes you have," she shot back, anger and guilt and her disturbed senses combining to drive her on, her desire to placate him gone. "You think I've joined forces with your friend Torgen to extract money from you."

The silence swirled around her like a living thing. His eyes, his body and his mouth seemed to be extensions of hers, as if he breathed in harmony with her and his blood beat through his veins in an angry rhythm that matched hers exactly. "Have you?"

"I've already told you I didn't know anything about this . . . and you didn't believe me. Why should you believe me now?"

Dressed casually, and relaxed against the door in an indolent stance that should have made him look lazy, he exuded vitality in waves. And something else. Something more primitive. And definitely more frightening. "Who was your source of information?"

"And old friend—"

"Male?"

"As it happens, yes, but—"

"Southern Florida seems to be littered with your old lovers."

"And there are such strict laws about that sort of thing," she retorted dryly. She took a deep breath, facing the fire in his eyes with a silver flame in her own. "He happens to be a friend, not a lover. . . . Not that it's any business of yours."

He absorbed her riposte without any visible sign of reaction. "And naturally, you turned to him in your time of need. Did he have something interesting for you?" Cay was wearing a pair of khaki shorts and a V-neck sweatshirt that made him look as cool and controlled as his voice.

The scent of roses began to fill the room, their perfume heavily provocative. "He thinks the man is Torgen, your old drummer. Is he right?"

He stood looking at her, his silence confirming Ferguson's guess.

"What reason did he give for my problems with my... old friend?"

"Money... and a woman."

"And you believe him?"

"He had no reason to lie."

"I wonder." Despite his apparent calm, a muscle worked at the side of his jaw. "What did he say exactly?"

Toni told him.

"And what about my... involvement with the woman? What did he say about that?"

"Nothing. He didn't need to."

"He didn't tell you she was Torgen's wife?"

She felt suddenly, overwhelmingly ill. "No."

He waited for something. She had no idea what. At last he grated, "Say what you're thinking."

She shook her head. She had no right to judge him.

"What, no condemnations, no stern looks of dismay? I wonder why."

His faintly taunting tone brought life to her tongue. "Perhaps because I'm not as quick to jump to conclusions about you as you are about me. Your friend's scruples don't impress me as being particularly stringent. My guess is that any woman willing to marry him might be just as unprincipled as he is. For all I know, she threw herself at you, and when you didn't accept her invitation into her bed, she lied to Torgen and told him you had."

When he finally spoke, only his mouth moved. "Your friend was an excellent source."

She didn't bother to deny again that Ferguson had told her about Torgen's wife. She was too busy absorbing the fact that she'd guessed what had happened so accurately. Several thousand keys inside her head clicked into place. No wonder Cay Sinclair didn't trust women. "You were betrayed by both of them." His silence told her she'd hit on the truth. "Did you care for her very much?"

"I thought she was a friend. I was wrong. It's ancient history," he said in that drawl that seemed to come naturally to him when he was feeling an emotion strongly. "These days—" his green-ice gaze played over her bikini-clad body with a cool assessment that wiped away the moment of sympathy she'd felt for him "—I try to be more realistic about women. Before I begin to believe their sweet lies, I ask myself what they have to gain from a relationship with me."

"From the sound of it, not very much," she said crisply, making a move to walk around him.

With one shift of his legs, which was so minute that it was almost invisible, he blocked the doorway, trapping her. "You think I have nothing to offer a woman?" She'd been wrong to challenge him on a sexual level, very wrong. She made a tentative attempt to push him aside. His eyes caught hers and the look in them stopped her. "What do you want, Toni? The two thousand dollars to pay off your debt? The possibility of more work? I can get you all that—and anything else you want."

Acting for all she was worth, dredging up a coolness she didn't feel, she said, "You have a very poor memory, Mr. Sinclair." Her skin seemed to burn. She hadn't told him the exact amount of her loan. Between last night and now, he'd been as busy investigating her as she had been him.

"Refresh it for me."

"I told you I wasn't for sale...at any price." As an exit line, it was a good one. There was only one problem. With him blocking the doorway, she couldn't go anywhere.

"There is an old saying, trite but true, that everybody has a price."

"That may be, but there isn't enough money in this world for you to buy me." He was so close that she could see the dark, expansive depths of his pupils and feel the warmth of his breath on her face.

"You sound almost as idealistic as I once was."

"Surely not." Her silver eyes sparkled with the light of battle.

"Are you still looking for love's young dream, for a man to come sweep you off your feet with words of undying love?"

She faced him, pride in the line of her chin, in the tilt of her head and in the dark silver of her eyes. "Whatever I think, whatever I am, whatever I feel has nothing to do with you."

His face changed, controlled by something subtle, yet primitive; starkly clear, yet secret. He pulled her into his arms and nowhere in the heated recesses of her mind could she find an urge to push him away. He threaded a hand up through her dark hair, and even though she knew he was readying her to accept his kiss, she couldn't move. Her lips felt heavy, swollen; they waited for his possession. "You're lonely," he murmured. "I've sensed that about you from the first moment I saw you." With a hand under her chin, he tilted her face up to his. "It's true, isn't it?"

In a daze, she said, "Yes."

"Let's be lonely together...."

His eyes told her he knew she was waiting to be kissed, and the lazy curve of his mouth betrayed his intention to draw out the agony. Then, as he moved closer—close enough that her warm breath mingled with his—his face changed subtly as if her nearness had melted away his need to tantalize and replaced it with a stronger, more basic hunger.

His lips brushed her... and for a moment it was still there—the cynicism, the premeditated assault on her senses, the coolly controlled passion that owed more to expertise than to desire.

As if she'd been waiting all her life for his mouth to touch hers, passion she hadn't known she possessed came tumbling out in a tidal wave, sweeping everything away—her inhibitions, his mistrust. She became his equal, a woman seeking to take what he gave and return it in full and ecstatic measure. His tongue flicked lightly at her lips, teasing her to gain entrance rather than forcing her to yield. His body fit against hers with a precision that was a prelude to another more intimate joining, and the feel of his hands on the bare small of her back took her from cool control to heated need in a microsecond.

He made a satisfied sound in his throat, as if she fed some deep, basic need in him, and lifted her away enough to murmur in a strained husky tone, "You tempt me to remember those words that delight a woman. Open, honey. Let me taste you. . . ."

He was no longer the gentle marauder. Cay tasted, explored, and, when he felt her mouth soften, he claimed what she'd surrendered with a masculine delight that was evident in each teasing thrust, each light flick of his tongue over hers. To give as she had given, he opened and invited her to plunder his mouth freely in the same fashion he had hers. She accepted what he gave joyously, savoring the taste of the wet silk of his mouth, her fingers tracing the shell of an ear, the slant of his jaw, the contour of the back of his neck.

He drew a ragged breath and pushed her away, and it was only then that she realized she'd been running her fingers lightly upward, teasing the fine strands of his hair.

"Are you trying to convince me you're worth any price you ask? If you are, you've nearly succeeded—"

Each word was like a blow to her senses, destroying the pleasure he'd given her a moment before. Flattening her hands against his chest, she shoved with all her strength. When she'd gained her freedom, she faced him, her breath coming hard and fast. "I'm not interested in anything you have to offer."

"You're lying."

"I...want...you...out...of...this...house. Now!"

An almost imperceptible change came over his features—a look of faint incredulity followed by a hardening, as if he'd made a decision and wasn't about to be swayed from it. "I'm not leaving."

Toni held her head high, but her knees were shaking. Instinct told her to hide that one visible sign of weakness or Sinclair would press for complete surrender, and this time she'd be powerless to stop him. They were alone in a quiet, cool house—alone...together. "If I'm the kind of woman you think I am, why do you want to protect me? If Torgen came to the door, I'd have thought you'd welcome your friend with open arms, escort him in and sit back and watch with great relish while he carried me off to the fishes."

"I've asked myself that question several times today."

"And what was the answer?" She really didn't care what he thought, she only knew she wanted him out of the house and away from her.

"If that happened, I'd know you were exactly what you claimed to be, an innocent victim of Torgen's machinations. And by then, it would be too late."

The darkness in his voice sent a shiver of fear up her spine. She couldn't and wouldn't acknowledge her fright. "Mr. Sinclair, you'd better go home and get some rest. Thoughts like that must be a terrible strain on your brain."

"Yes," he said, watching her, "they are." His eyes flickered over her face, and he seemed to come to a decision. "If it's any consolation to you, I've hired two men to watch the house. You can now sleep upstairs in your own bed." At the flash of relief in her eyes, he shook his head. "No, don't get your hopes up. I'm not leaving. I'm staying right here. But you won't have to sleep with me."

"You're so kind."

Lazily running his insolent gaze over her, he said, "You'd better go upstairs and get out of that bikini before you catch . . . cold. . . . And, Toni—"

He'd only said her name, but hearing him say it did strange things to her.

"What is it?"

"Be careful . . . upstairs. Stay away from the windows. And don't lock your door. And if you hear anything . . . scream. I'll be there in two seconds."

His words were meant to reassure her. They didn't.

"All right."

THE LANGUOR, the longing, came like a thief in the night. Toni was a mature woman, and she'd been kissed and caressed in a prelude to lovemaking. Now she lay in her bed wanting . . . him.

She rolled over and tried to block the thought from her mind. It was a useless, senseless notion, born on the waves of the romantic dreams he'd accused her of having. Romantic dreams. Her mind produced a picture of Cay Sinclair as he'd looked five years before.

She'd been twenty-four that summer, and she'd saved her money and taken a bus from Los Angeles to New York during the hottest days of July. Cay Sinclair was appearing in what was rumored to be his last public concert in New York City, and she'd wanted to be there.

The concert was in Central Park. The heat hadn't abated. Standing on the grass, the perspiration running down her back, she'd watched him play. His skin as wet as hers, he'd performed for three hours to a gargantuan crowd. Though she wasn't a musician, she knew it was a truly great performance and that she would never again hear music like this.

Toni had wondered if it was true—if he was retiring. She wouldn't be surprised if he was. How much longer could he go on draining himself like this with an exhausting schedule of live concerts? She stood squeezed in the crowd, watching him with a bittersweet enjoyment. He played with his head thrown back and his face twisted in an inner agony and ecstasy, the depth of which she could only guess. Though the audience stayed as quiet as a church congregation while he played and exploded in a frenzy of clapping and cheering when he stopped, somehow he didn't look as if he were enjoying himself.

The crowd didn't notice or care. He was a star—a man raised to a level above all others, a man his fans idolized because of his ability to do what they wanted to do and couldn't.

He was a lonely man. She'd recognized that in him because she knew what it was like to be lonely.

And he'd recognized that in her. Those soft words that had discovered the secret of her life had nearly been her undoing.

A memory she'd put out of her mind flashed before her eyes, something that had happened when the New York concert ended and he'd tried to walk away. She'd fought through the crowd to reach him only to have a security guard push her aside. But he'd turned, and for a moment she'd thought he'd seen her, that he'd picked out her face in the crowd.

She did have romantic dreams. Only now did she realize they were focused on one man . . . and had been ever since the day she'd watched Cay Sinclair playing in Central Park.

4

TONI DRUMMED a rat-a-tat rhythm on the back of the velvet couch with her fingers and stared up at the smiling lady who lay there showing all her teeth. It wasn't fair for one woman to be that beautiful and have the self-confidence to display her feminine charms with such panache.

Well, there were a lot of things in life that were unfair. She'd learned early about unfairness. There was that umpire who'd called her brother, Satch, out on second base in the last game he ever played for his alma mater.

She circled the couch, found the two handles to pull out the bed and snatched the sheets off the mattress. There was another thing that was unfair. It was unfair that Sinclair has spent the night here in this house, and it was totally unfair of him to think she was after him for his money.

She walked through the kitchen into the laundry room and stuffed the sheets in the washing machine, wishing she could stuff Sinclair in with them. Punching buttons furiously, she told herself the former rock star and that umpire had a lot in common. They were both blind and needed their heads examined.

Cool reason told her that allowing Cay Sinclair to spend the night in the same house for as many days as he wanted would eventually vindicate her. Hot temper told her it didn't matter what he thought of her and that she ought to throw the bum out.

Maybe she should give Cay the same treatment she'd given the umpire. She had flown at the man and though people tried to deflect her and protect him, he'd emerged from the fracas with a black eye. Satch had called her Toni the Tiger for days after that.

When the sheets were dry and back on the bed, the rest of the morning spent itself in rubber band minutes that stretched into interminable hours. She went to the beach in the afternoon with Liz, but in her mind, she was bracing herself for the moment when Sinclair walked into the house.

But when he appeared at the door that evening, she realized that all the time in the world wouldn't have been enough to prepare her for the sight of Cay Sinclair. Like the creatures in Pandora's box, the dreams and thoughts of the night before flew up from their hiding places.

Angry at herself and at him for drawing her into the coil of his life when she didn't belong there, Toni spent the rest of the evening avoiding him, executing her maneuvers with the finesse of a four-star general. When he was in the kitchen, she was in the living room. If he came into the living room, she went upstairs.

But he'd found the stereo system and her collection of records. On Tuesday night after he'd been sitting in the living room alone for an hour while she'd been upstairs trying to read a boring book, the music of Brahms curled up the stairway. On Wednesday he played her entire, uncut version of Gershwin's *American in Paris*. On Thursday, he listened to Beethoven's *Ninth*, and as if an uncanny telepathy existed between them, he played the last movement over again . . . just as she always did. Unlike her, he studiously avoided playing anything of his own, even though there was a huge selection. She had everything he'd ever recorded, including his earlier releases.

Trips to the beach with Liz during the day helped to relieve the tension. Her skin turned a golden brown, contrasting with her black hair to give her a pagan look.

When Sinclair arrived on Thursday evening, as usual, she immediately started up the stairs.

"Toni," he called. Caught on the stairs and unable to pretend she hadn't heard him, she turned.

"Is my music . . . bothering you?"

He was asking more than that. He was asking her to look at him, to talk to him. He was asking for a truce.

"No," she said, "it doesn't bother me at all," and continued up the stairs.

On Friday morning Toni woke with a sense of relief. She had work to do. The second concert was scheduled for Sunday afternoon, and since it was to be held on the porch of Hemingway House, she was going over this afternoon to look at the concert site.

Around noon the music of Ravel's *Bolero* filled the house. Liz snatched up a wilting rose from the vase of flowers that Toni knew she should have discarded two days ago but hadn't. The redheaded senorita clenched the rose stem in her teeth and did a turn around the kitchen, clicking her heels and humming with the music.

"Would you stop?" Toni regarded her with dark eyes. "You're scattering rose petals all over the floor."

Liz ignored Toni's slightly uncivil request. She was a relentless optimist and thought the whole world should be happy. Normally Toni adored Liz's sunny, even-tempered nature ... and it only took her a second to regret her outburst. Liz didn't seem to mind. "I'm exercising." Dipping her chin, Liz flashed a sultry glance at Toni from under her eyelashes.

As she hunched her shoulders and stared at Liz over the rim of her coffee cup, Toni thought, *This has been the longest week of my life.* Was Sinclair ever going to admit defeat and stop coming to the house? And was he ever going to stop playing her favorite music? "What, exactly, are you exercising?"

Cheerfully ignoring Toni's lack of enthusiasm, Liz sent a beatific smile zinging her way. Raising her arms, she began clicking her fingers as if they held castanets. Her eyes cast sultry stares at Toni over the rose, which by now had exactly three petals clinging to the stem.

When Toni didn't respond, Liz stopped dancing and took the rose out of her mouth. "I'm trying to get you in the mood for your visit to the house of Hemingway, that man's man who loved bullfighting and women and deep-sea fishing and women—"

"Spare me the biographical sketch."

"How do you feel about mysteries?" Liz leaned over her and said in a Greta Garbo voice, "There were questions to be asked, questions that no one wanted to answer, questions that would cause somebody trouble.

Such as . . . why is the lovely young lady so glum this morning?"

"Please. I'm just not in the mood."

"That's because you're not trying." Dropping into the chair beside her, Liz said, "Come on, Toni, where's your sense of humor? What's the matter? Didn't you sleep well?"

"Now that you mention it, no."

"Neither did I," Liz replied, lifting her shoulders and smiling at Toni with a blaze of sheer happiness. "Isn't love wonderful?"

"Wonderful." The word crackled with sarcasm.

"Things aren't going right with you and Cay." Liz tilted her head and studied Toni.

Toni sat back in the chair and folded her arms. Liz's face was flushed with earnestness and enthusiasm. Looking at her, Toni suddenly felt old. "Things aren't going, period."

"But you do like him, don't you?"

"Not particularly," Toni said dryly.

"But . . . but you said such nice things about him before you met him, about how much you admired his music and how great you thought he was and how glad you were that you were going to be able to hear him play in concert again."

"That was before I met him."

"You mean you don't like him now? Even when he's been coming here every night?"

"No, I don't like him now. I tolerate him coming here because I have to work with him, that's all."

To Toni's amazement, Liz flushed and looked away. "I thought you liked him. I thought you wanted to be with him."

"Liz, what is it? Is there something I should know about?"

For a moment, Toni thought Liz wasn't going to answer her. Then in a rush, Liz said, "I'm not going with you to Hemingway House this afternoon. He is."

Toni sat up. "What?"

"This morning he asked me what your schedule was." At Toni's expression, Liz hurriedly added, "He always does, there's nothing new in that."

"*Et tu, Brute*," Toni murmured.

"What did you say?"

"Nothing. Go on."

"Well, there isn't any more. Except that he wanted me to wait and not say anything to you, and he'd just show up here at the right time. I couldn't do that. I didn't want you to think I was ... letting you down." Liz's eyes pleaded for understanding.

"Thank you for that."

"He's giving me the afternoon off. I'm going to the beach with Tommy. Is that okay?"

She looked anxious and contrite and Toni knew now that the elaborate dance had been a way for Liz to build up her courage. That was another thing to blame Sinclair for. Before, she and Liz never had any secrets from each other. They had established a relationship based on honesty and trust.

But here was another it-wasn't-fair. It wasn't fair to deprive Liz of an afternoon at the beach with her man. Toni steeled herself. "Of course it's okay. Why shouldn't he go with me to look over the house? We're business acquaintances, doing a job together."

"Oh, great." Liz's relief was evident in her flashing smile, her sudden relaxation. "Now, why don't you go upstairs and start getting ready? You can wear my gold necklace. It will look great with your tan."

Toni rose from the table, her eyes on the drooping flowers. She lifted them out of the vase and disposed of them quickly without looking at them. "I won't need a necklace. I'll just wear the noose I'm putting my head into."

"THIS, AS YOU CAN SEE," the tour guide intoned in a way that told Toni she had given this same speech too many times before, "is the Hemingways' bedroom."

Toni wasn't looking at the Hemingways' bedroom. She was staring out the window at the carriage house where Hemingway had done his writing, but she wasn't thinking about the famous author. She was thinking that she was a fool. Why had she climbed into Sinclair's gray Toyota and come with him to this house? And why had she fallen in with his suggestion that they take a guided tour and see the entire house as long as they were there?

Pride had made her do it. Pride and a foolish need to prove to him somehow that his presence didn't bother her in the slightest.

But it did. There were a dozen other people in the room listening to the tour guide, but Toni was as aware of Cay as she was of the gold necklace of Liz's that she was wearing.

"Notice the size of the bed." The guide continued with the story, saying that Pauline Hemingway had been one of the first people to think of installing two single beds under one headboard to give the appearance of a double.

There was more, something about the headboard being a monastery gate Hemingway had brought back from Spain. Toni stopped listening and wandered away from the group. A French door led to the balcony where Hemingway had installed the catwalk that he used to go from the bedroom to his studio in the carriage house. The catwalk was gone, swept away by a hurricane, and the balcony was fully enclosed by a waist-high railing. Toni stepped through the doorway and walked into the light of the late-afternoon sun. Its heat was blocked in the shade from the trees surrounding the house.

"Toni."

Her fingers curled around the sun-warmed wrought iron. Bathed in a heated warmth that was related to the husky depth of that now familiar voice, she made no response.

"You missed seeing the Picasso cat." She didn't move. "Toni, look at me." He'd followed her outside, and from the sound of his voice, he was standing close behind her. Her nerves tightened in an exquisite tension, but she didn't acknowledge his presence. He said throatily, "What would you consider a proper apology? My head on a platter?"

She swung around and leaned back against the railing, facing him. "That would be a nice start."

In a soft white shirt and dark, tailored pants, he looked considerably cooler than she felt.

"But a little difficult for me to achieve," he replied.

The sudden absence of the noisy shuffling of feet and the chatter of other people brought an intimate quietness to the balcony. Midafternoon shadows played over Cay's face. Was it her imagination or was there a tension in his mouth, a hint of pain in his eyes?

She swung away from him and clenched the railing again. "I have a feeling that it would be easier for you to do than to admit you've made a mistake."

"I'm not immune to mistakes," he said roughly. "I've made my share of them."

He came to stand next to her, but he wasn't looking at her. He was gazing out at the view. She turned slightly to study his profile. "And you'll go on making them as long as you keep judging the people you meet by the ones you've known before."

She could see that he was surprised at her bluntness. "You *do* want my head on a platter, don't you?"

"No," she said coolly, her eyes on his. "I don't want anything from you."

Now it was his hands that clasped the railing, his head that was turned, his eyes that avoided hers by staring down into the yard below. Off to one side, an old banyan tree stood tied to the ground a million times over by its own long-fingered branches.

"When we were downstairs, what novel did they say Hemingway wrote while he lived here?" he finally said.

"*To Have and Have Not.*"

"Yes," he murmured, turning to look at her.

Toni swung away. "He must have had a better view then, before the trees grew so tall."

"What do you suppose he saw?" Clearly humoring her, he turned his back to the railing and leaned against it, watching her, a strange tension emanating from him.

She struggled to follow his waltz step into neutral territory. "Probably a panorama—the ocean, the Gulf, Old Town—a world of his own."

"Like the one he created in his book."

"Yes, I suppose."

"A world of illusion, a pretty story world where people can trust each other or not according to his whim...a world about as real as the one you create with your sound equipment."

"Whereas you deal strictly in facts," she returned with biting clarity.

"I deal in honesty." Facing forward again, Cay stared into the distance at the tops of the buildings and the fronds of the palm trees. "I've spent this week finding out a truth about myself." He turned to her, his eyes dark, compelling. "I've discovered I don't give a damn if you're conspiring with Torgen or even if you're the brains behind it. I don't care about what you've done or what you are. That all happened before we met. You didn't know me then...and I didn't know you." Slanted shadows played over him, dappling his classic nose, his strong, well-shaped jaw, the smooth line of his cheek. "But now that we've met, I know I can forgive you anything—except a lie. If you have something to tell me, do it now. I promise there will be no repercussions."

"You mean," she replied, rounding on him furiously, "that if I said I was part of the conspiracy to threaten and defraud you, you would accept that and let me walk away scot-free?"

He held her gaze for a moment and then suddenly turned back to the railing. "I wouldn't prosecute, but I wouldn't let you walk away."

"Excuse me." The tour guide stood on the lawn below looking up at Toni and Cay, a frown on her face. "If you'll please come down and join us, we're going to continue the tour with a trip up to the studio." She turned back to her more obedient charges, who were clustered around her. "Now I must ask you, because the steps are narrow, to go up one at a time. We are in the process of collecting funds for the renovation of the studio, but nothing has been done at the present time...."

One or two curious faces were still turned toward them. Toni moved back against the wall, instinctively disliking the way she and Cay had become the object of the crowd's curiosity.

Inside the bedroom, Cay's voice halted her. "I'd like an answer to my question."

Caught between a strange belief that she'd somehow misunderstood him and the urge to fly at him, she said icily, "You had the answer to your question days ago."

"You refuse to admit the truth."

"Truth!" she snapped. "It's your truth, not my truth. And your truth is a lie!"

"I ... want to believe that."

"No, you don't. It doesn't fit in with your theories about people in general and women in particular."

She whirled away from him, furious with him and angrier yet with herself for not recognizing the futility of talking to a man with a closed mind. Toni wanted to walk out of the house and keep on going, but she couldn't. He still hadn't told her the things she needed to know about Sunday's concert.

The physical act of walking ahead of Cay down the stairs, through the den and onto the porch helped her to cool her temper enough to say, "What are your plans for Sunday?"

He hesitated for a moment as if he had something else to say, but when he saw the look in her eyes, he said coolly, "The concert is going to be held here, away from the banyan tree. The quartet will set up on this corner so the audience can fan out on the lawn." Cay stepped down off the porch and walked away from the house, heading toward the banyan tree. Toni followed. "You can run a power line out here from the den. How far out will you need to put your speakers?"

A cat scampered in front of them, one of the many that hung around the house in droves. They were descendants, so the guide had told them, of Hemingway's own cats and wore the proof of their ancestry on their feet in their six toes. Toni caught Cay's arm. "Wait a minute. Don't walk that way."

He stopped and turned, his face showing his surprise at her spontaneous clutching of his arm. Immediately she pulled her hand away. "Why not?" he asked, his eyes playing over her face in evident curiosity.

She wished she hadn't said anything, but she hadn't been able to stop herself. "Just . . . don't."

He stared at her for a moment and then turned and looked at the cat scampering away from them at breakneck speed. A black cat . . . and Toni had stopped him from crossing its path. He raised a dark eyebrow. "You're superstitious?"

"Among my many other sins, yes."

"Don't you think your concern for me is a little inconsistent?"

"Do you mean combined with my efforts to defraud you or with my general opinion of you?" Exasperated, she brushed at a black lock of hair, which had escaped her decorative comb. The heat in the garden was intense and she felt hot and furious and . . . cornered. "I don't wish bad luck on anybody, not even—" her eyes swept over him "—my worst enemy."

She turned and walked away from him a few paces and her profile and the way her body moved in the yellow sundress stirred an old memory—a memory so vague he could hardly recall it. But it was there. A woman with her hair in a long black braid, her face as bathed with perspiration as his own, calling out something to him and then disappearing into the crowd.

Yes, there had been a crowd, and it had been as high-summer hot as it was today, and he'd been thinking that this was the last time he'd put himself through this particular torture chamber—it was his last concert. Toni had been there. She'd looked a little younger, maybe because of the braid, but the face and the body and the smooth, controlled way of walking were exactly the same. To her back, he said softly, "Once long ago, on a hot summer day, you wished me good luck. At my last concert in New York City."

She swiveled slowly to face him. He watched her, wondering if she would deny it. If she did, she would be lying.

"How on earth did you remember that?"

"You said it with more feeling then most people do, as if you really meant it. When I met you for the first time last Saturday, I wondered why you looked familiar to me," Cay said. And she had. Right from the first, she'd haunted him.

"I was nothing but a face in the crowd to you." Toni lifted her head.

Cay ignored her words. "If you were there that day, you must have seen Torgen."

The surprise and pleasure she'd felt because he remembered her left in a rush. He'd found a new reason to condemn her. She went cold inside. "I suppose I did."

"And you still didn't recognize him when he stopped us on the street the other night?" At the shake of her head, he said blandly. "I suppose that's not surprising, considering the way he was dressed."

"What a concession," she replied hotly. "What did you think? That I hung around to talk to him that day and planned all this so I could turn up in your life five years later? I should think that would stretch even your imagination!"

"I know you didn't stay to talk to him that day." His face was smooth, composed. She hadn't a clue to his thoughts.

"How could you possibly know that?"

"Because I sent one of my roadies after you. He saw you boarding a bus for Los Angeles, and then he lost you."

He was telling the truth, she thought dazedly. There was no breeze in the yard; the banyan tree and the hedge around the lot didn't allow it. He looked deadly serious . . . and deadly beautiful.

"If he had found me, what would he have done?"

"Invited you to come and have dinner with me." At the look in her eyes, he added, "Nothing more than that."

"Were you in the habit of . . . doing that?" Waiting for his answer, she was filled with a swirl of conflicting emotions.

"No. I'd never done it before. The entire crew thought I was crazy." He took a step toward her. "Toni. Have that dinner with me now."

"I can't think of one reason why I should—"

"I can think of ten. I've had all I can take of sitting in that house alone while you hide out upstairs. We're both hungry, and we need a chance to get to know each other better."

She thought for a moment, looking at him. "That's only three reasons."

Cay told himself not to get too excited. She was relenting, but the battle wasn't over. "Come with me and I'll work on the other seven while we eat. Be fair. Is it any wonder I find it hard to trust you? You haven't given me a chance to get to know you. We had one dinner together, and since then, you've hardly spoken to me."

He couldn't know that he'd found her weak point. Maybe she hadn't been fair. Maybe if she went out with him and talked to him, he would lay aside his mistrust and they could return to a more amiable relationship. Maybe he would see that she meant him no harm, and he would relax his surveillance of her. And maybe he would stop coming into her house nights and playing music that drove her out of her mind. And maybe she would find a way to obliterate that one kiss from her memory, just as it seemed he had. "Did you have any place special in mind?"

"There's a new restaurant in Old Town I thought you might enjoy."

As he escorted her to the car, carefully not touching her, Cay knew he'd scored a major victory. He wasn't exactly sure what had tipped the scales, whether it was his appeal to her sense of justice or simply the prospect of having a meal out. Whatever it was, he thanked the gods who'd sent that cat strolling across his path.

Beside him, Toni moved with that easy grace he had noticed the first night on the pier. Why hadn't he recognized her then? Probably because she was working as a sound engineer, and so he hadn't thought of her as a fan. But during the week he'd spent in her house, he'd gone through her record collection and discovered that she owned every album he'd ever recorded, including a rare and rather obscure one he'd made early in his career. His subconscious must have been chewing on that, and adding Morry's suspicions to his own, he'd come to the wrong conclusion that she had been following his career for a long time, waiting for a chance to approach him.

Now he'd learned the truth, that she was what she seemed to be—a fan. He accepted the fact that people liked his music, but it didn't seem real to him. He couldn't imagine people playing his records, listening to his music when he wasn't there. It was one of those things that seemed obvious, yet he couldn't believe it was true.

Perhaps Toni's innocence was just as obvious.

Key West people seemed to have a love for second-story living, Toni thought as Cay escorted her into the air-conditioned coolness of a popular dining room nestled on the top floor of a historic commercial building.

"Do you have reservations?" a black-jacketed maître d' asked.

Nerves prickled along Toni's arm. Had Cay been so sure of her?

"No," Cay said smoothly. "How long will it be?"

"Not long. Your name, sir?" When Cay told him, there was no sign of recognition. To his credit, Toni decided, Sinclair didn't look in the least perturbed. Perhaps since his drop from public life, he'd grown used to that. Instead of protesting or trying to bribe or intimidate the man, Cay led Toni to the bar and pulled out a plush maroon velvet stool with spindly legs and a cane back and, with a hand on her elbow, helped her into it.

When she was settled, she made a small movement asking for release. He let go of her instantly. They ordered their drinks and were served immediately. Toni sipped her gin and tonic, thinking she needed its cool sting on her throat. Cay didn't take the stool next to her. He stood beside her, his back to the bar, one arm draped across the top of her stool, his Manhattan in easy reach.

So, unfortunately, was she. His casually relaxed arm controlled the angle of her seat, and Cay was keeping her turned toward him, so that her knees were bumping against his left inner thigh. She propped an elbow on the armrest and lifted the glass to her lips. The dryness in her throat was caused by more than the heat of the afternoon.

Knees weren't supposed to be sensitive. Yet through the gauze of her dress and the soft linen of his trousers, she could feel the latent power in his long thigh muscle.

Was he standing so close on purpose? She didn't know. And if she moved away, she would be admitting how much he disturbed her.

Out of the corner of her eye, she saw a reflection of Cay in the bar mirror. She hadn't noticed the side of his head before. He had a rather small ear for a man, perfectly shaped, his dark glossy hair carelessly tousled around it. The strong line of his jaw and throat revealed his lithe fitness.

"I like your hair," Cay said. "You look cool like that with it caught up away from your face."

She'd been looking at him in the mirror, but he'd been gazing directly at her, studying the soft hollow of her throat where Liz's necklace lay, taking in the bare curve of her shoulder and neck above the bodice of her sundress. Her eyes flashed to his, and there, unconcealed, lay a dark, inciting challenge. "Thank you," she murmured, her eyes as cool as his were heated. "I'm glad you like it."

"You see? Civilized conversation with me isn't that difficult, if you put your mind to it. In fact, I have a feeling you could do anything you put your mind to."

Could she? Could she forget the way his mouth had felt on hers? Even now, looking at him, she remembered the shape and feel of it, the texture, the fullness, the persistent tenderness. She'd dissolved into him willingly, oh so willingly, and for an instant, the dream man and the real man had merged into something more powerful than her image of either of them. Now he was so close that she could see his eyes move as they wandered over her face, and she knew that if she tried for the rest of her life, she would never forget him.

She broke eye contact and sipped her drink, wishing that Cay had been more forceful about insisting on a table. Why hadn't he? This was a supreme kind of torture, being so close to him in this luxurious bar that was rapidly filling with people. Somehow, the more people crowded in next to her at the bar, the more she felt isolated in a bubble world that included only Cay.

A man walking by jostled him. A lesser man might have fallen against her in a clumsy attempt to get physically closer. Cay's body was unyielding steel, and even though he'd been caught off guard, he braced himself and took the full brunt of the blow without leaning into her.

He had protected her from the intruder . . . and from himself. It was an act of thoughtfulness that nearly undid all of Toni's fine resolve. How could she deal with a man like this who seemed so cynical and yet had such deep reserves of instinctive kindness?

Damn! He'd nearly fallen on her, and if he had, they'd have gone back to square one. He'd caught himself just in time. When he'd looked up, he'd watched her eyes go smoky gray, the pupils dark and deep. Did she hate the thought of physical contact with him so much that her body reacted with a defense mechanism automatically?

It was obvious Toni didn't want to be here with him. Yet she was. Call it fate or luck or circumstance, she was here.

The thought that he'd met her again after five years by a capricious whim of fate disturbed him. If she hadn't been in debt and desperate for work, she'd never have come to Key West.

If she hadn't been in debt and desperate for work, he'd never have suspected her.

None of it made any sense. He only knew he'd made the decision to pursue her because...she interested him. He couldn't remember the last time he'd felt this way about a woman.

It wasn't like him to actually pursue a woman. After Elaine had divorced him and stripped him of his pride and his bank account, he'd taken women or left them, according to their availability and his inclination. For the women who'd flocked around him had been like his wife, interested in him because of who he was rather than what he was.

They had used him, and at the time, it hadn't mattered. Nothing had mattered but his music. It was the only thing that made any sense. He'd worked hard and played hard and had let life pour its bounty over him, taking what it offered—money, women, recognition. He'd been on a merry-go-round of endless months of working, and monotonous days and nights on the road. At a tour's end, he'd host a party for all the people who'd toured with him and half a hundred who hadn't. Of those who came, he wouldn't know a fourth. Inevitably one of the women would stay and spend the night . . . or the week . . . or the month.

In the end it had been his all-night composing sessions that had brought him back to sanity. Music, the kind of music that was gut honest, real, became the center of his universe. Those solitary sessions spent grappling with finding the right chord, the right melody, the right sound, made him decide to withdraw from performing in public.

He'd found a peace he could live with. He'd rediscovered the world, listened to the birds sing, looked at the color of the grass, breathed in deeply of the air. He had a home for every season—the one in Key West for winter, one in New York City for the spring and fall, and one in the Colorado mountains for high summer. Yes, he had one for each season, but all of them were for his pride. It made him feel good to buy an expensive piece of real estate and know he'd earned it by his own efforts. He'd thought he had everything he'd ever wanted. Until now.

Cay lifted his drink to his lips, and when he'd quenched his thirst, he indulged himself in watching her. He liked everything about Toni—her short dark hair, the proud lift of her chin, her slender body. She was wearing a gold necklace that gleamed against her tanned skin and accented the graceful line of her throat. His mind taunted him with images of her wearing nothing but that necklace. . . .

"Mr. Sinclair? Your table is ready now. If you'd follow me, please?"

5

TONI FINISHED EATING and, sated, stopped fighting the assault on her senses of the wine and the food and the decor, which was so Spanish that it made her think of Liz dancing around the kitchen with the rose in her teeth. There were no traditional roses to be found here. On the wall, crimson lilies as big as kites flared against a background of black bamboo in a painting that was dramatic and eye-catching. Beneath her full-skirted gauze dress, the wine velvet of the banquette seemed to reach out and cling. The table linen was mauve; the crystal Venetian. The food, the wine cooling in the bucket beside her, the soft piano music were perfect—as perfect as the politeness in Cay's eyes.

He lounged beside her, staying at the respectful distance he'd maintained all evening, as relaxed as she was wound tight. He'd inquired if the wine was to her liking, asked if she wanted the waiter to bring another slice of lemon, offered to cut her a slice of bread. She'd said yes to everything, vowing to treat him just as urbanely as he did her, but she was totally incapable of taking her eyes off him as he complied with her requests. He cut the bread deftly, easily, his hands unconsciously sensual in the use of the cutlery.

Toni wasn't the only one who couldn't keep her eyes off Cay. A woman seated at the next table, holding a toddler in her arms, glanced at him from time to time as if she recognized him, but she didn't speak to him or intrude on his privacy. In some subtle way, Cay discouraged it.

Toni laid her fork on her plate and daubed her napkin against her mouth, preparing herself to return politeness for politeness. "The meal was delicious. Thank you."

"You're welcome." He was the essence of good manners.

Cay flexed the muscles in his legs and thought about what a failure the dinner had been. He hated failure. When he was composing music, he'd learned that the best way to solve a creative problem was to suspend fear and let his mind float free, allowing space for the intuitive solution to flash into his mind.

Flashes of inspiration eluded him tonight. His every action, every word, seemed to compound her dislike for him.

The whole thing was a puzzle he couldn't put together. Was she innocent or was she playing a game with more skill than he had dreamed possible? He was ninety-nine percent sure that she wasn't lying. If only he could wipe out the minuscule doubt that remained.

What had happened to Torgen? In this last week, the man seemed to have vanished with the ocean breeze. Was he hatching some new plot?

The vague thought crossed Cay's mind that they were unprotected, seated as they were on a raised dais near an aisle, where waiters passed by them constantly. They had privacy behind them created by a half wall, but a dropped ceiling of decorative black glass reflected the heads of the family party who sat facing them a few feet away. The woman who kept looking at him as if she recognized him held a toddler in her arms, a blond cherub whose sex Cay had identified tentatively as male.

His eyes flickered to Toni. She was watching the child, and when the little imp gurgled with laughter, her face softened in a way that it hadn't all evening. He felt a sudden, inexplicable stab of jealousy. A child she didn't even know could accomplish what he hadn't been able to do with three-quarters of a bottle of Dom Perignon, two hours of excellent cuisine and soft music.

"Would you care for some more wine?"

To Toni's ears, Cay sounded brusque, annoyed. He'd probably grown tired of being polite and wanted to bring the evening to an end. She should take pity on him and refuse so he could ask for the check as he obviously longed to do. The urge to make him suffer a little longer made her say, "Yes, please." She lifted her wineglass and watched him tilt the bottle and pour the wine with the same easy grace he did everything.

When he'd filled his own glass and returned the wine to the ice bucket, Toni watched him sit back and frown slightly as his eyes wandered away from her back to the child. For some reason the youngster seemed to displease him. Didn't he like children?

Cay traced a fingertip absently around the foot of his wineglass and wondered why his mind wouldn't serve up a solution to this problem. How could he break through that seemingly impenetrable barrier she'd put between them? He watched her lift her glass to her lips, totally absorbed in the capability of her slim hands, which was why he didn't see Torgen until it was too late. Torgen's grimy fingers had already wrapped themselves around the wine bottle, raised it and brought it smashing down against the edge of the bucket.

Glass cracked and flew. A woman screamed. Something flicked his face, glass or wine, he wasn't sure which. Anger and adrenaline poured through him in equal amounts. What a fool he'd been to give in to his own optimistic wish that Torgen had given up. He'd dropped his guard, and he'd been caught napping. But not for long.

Cay was off the banquette and on his feet when Torgen cried, "Don't come any closer."

Torgen's hand—the hand that had once slammed out machine-gun rhythms on a drumhead with inhuman speed—held the jagged edge of the bottle inches from Toni's cheek. She went instantly rigid, as still and as waxy pale as a mannequin. Only her eyes moved. They connected with his, all the polite barriers gone, a silent cry of shock in their silver depths that wrenched his insides. Cay breathed out a succinct word.

Torgen laughed. "What's the matter, Sinclair? Didn't you expect to see me again? I made you a promise, remember?" The glass moved an inch closer to Toni's cheek.

Fury tore at Cay, making his muscles rigid with frustration. He whipped his mind to calmness and ordered up cold, reasonable thought. He wanted to hit Torgen, but he didn't dare. "Let her go," he said through clenched teeth.

"No," said Torgen, grinning. "I don't think I will."

"You hurt her and I'll kill you."

In response to Cay's threat, Torgen pulled back and faked a jab at Toni, which for one horrible moment looked as if it were going to connect with her cheek. She shrank back, and her reaction and Torgen's twisted need to torment Cay rather than actually maim her kept those lethal edges from touching her face, but Cay cursed himself for a fool. Torgen's mind had deteriorated since Cay had last seen him. The man was totally mad. The feathered hat was gone, replaced by a dark artist's beret, and beneath the black bush of hair sticking out from under the rim of cloth, Torgen's eyes glittered with the uncanny alertness of a deranged mind.

To Toni, it was a nightmare in blurred motion. Torgen had been unreal to her before, a comic book character. He was real now. A force to contend with. Cay was saying something else to him, and that low, threatening tone simmered with a controlled violence that should have terrified any man. Torgen seemed unaffected. He laughed at Cay, and the jagged glass didn't move an inch away from Toni's face.

Afraid to move a microinch, she kept her head exactly where it was and forced her eyes to look down. Was there anything on the table she could use to deflect him? The knife that Cay had used to cut the bread was too far away. Her own wineglass was full, but how could she pick it up without alerting Torgen?

Out of the corner of her eye, Toni saw the toddler sliding down from the banquette, his eyes alive with curiosity, his chubby feet sending him on a direct path toward Torgen. The woman who'd been holding him

screamed, "My baby, my baby!" Torgen's eyes flickered sideways. Instantly Cay moved a step toward the
child.

With the well-coordinated ease of a drummer, Torgen shifted the bottle to his other hand and lunged at
Cay, poking the jagged edge in his face. "Don't you
move," he ordered.

"You touch that child and I'll see to it that you never
hold a drumstick in that hand again," Cay said in a
voice that was as deadly cold as a cobra's skin.

"I'm not interested in a kid—"

That was all Toni needed to hear. Before Torgen realized her intent, she flew off the seat, scooped up the
child and dumped him into his mother's arms, extri-
cating the squawling toddler's fingers from her full
skirt.

The woman burst into grateful tears. Toni wasn't listening. She was thinking about that wealth of material
in her skirt....

As the woman sobbed, she heard Cay's low voice
from over her shoulder say, "Run, Toni. Now—"

Torgen didn't allow Cay to finish. The bottle moved
an inch closer to Cay's face. "You move one step and he
gets it."

"Get out of here, Toni," Cay ordered her through
gritted teeth.

"You take one step," Torgen threatened, "and he'll
never play in public again because no one will be able
to stand looking at him. You've done your good deed,
now cool it and get back over here."

"Whatever you say," said Toni, ignoring Cay's
throaty curse and moving to stand with her back to

their table. With her full skirt hiding her movements from Torgen's view, she groped behind her for her wineglass. "I'm cool. You're the one who's overheated."

Her words enraged him, just as she'd hoped they would, and while he was caught in the throes of his anger, she grabbed her glass and tossed the contents straight into Torgen's eyes. He let the broken bottle crash to the floor, cursed, shook his head and rubbed his eyes with his fists and stepped back, but he was too late in his defense. Cay quickly grabbed him.

From behind the screen came a shout. The woman holding the child screamed again and there was the sound of running feet. A male voice commanded that someone call the police. A man in a uniform materialized beside Cay and said, "Security. What's going on here?"

Torgen's face became a canny mask of relief. "Officer, I'm very glad to see you. I was dining with my lady friend when this man came up and started threatening me—"

Knocked off balance by Torgen's audacity, Toni was speechless. Cay uttered a sound of rage and lunged at Torgen and the security guard grabbed Cay and pulled him away. "Hold on, now." Cay twisted loose from the guard's grip, but that was all the distraction Torgen needed. He whirled, and in the next instant, he was gone.

"You damned fool, now look what you've done!" His face taut with fury, Cay rounded on the security guard. "He's the one you want, not me. Don't just stand there. Go after him."

The man was implacable. "Not until I find out what's going on."

"You stupid idiot, he's a crazy man, and you've let him get away. Toni, are you all right?" Cay turned to her, his green eyes anxious.

His concern warmed her, chased away the cold fear. "I'm . . . all right. I was just worried about the child." *And you.*

Seeing her go limp with relief, Cay ground his teeth in helpless rage. He ached to race after Torgen, but he knew it was hopeless to give chase when the wily rabbit had such a head start, and he couldn't leave Toni in the hands of this ape who obviously didn't have enough brains to come in out of the rain.

Compounding Cay's low opinion of him the guard said, "You'll have to come down to the police station with me and file a report—"

"If you don't let us walk out of here there'll be two incidents to report."

The guard hesitated, his eyes taking in Cay's tall, leanly fit body and the barely contained anger in his face, and he released his hold. Tossing a bill on the table to pay for their meal, Cay pulled Toni from the dining room with a speed she supposed he had learned as a rock star while fleeing delirious fans. His long-legged strides swept her down the stairs and into his car.

When she saw where he was headed, she said, "Aren't we supposed to be going to the police station?"

"I'll call them from the house."

She looked away from him and stared out the side window. "You . . . can't believe I had anything to do with this."

"I don't," he said shortly as if he didn't want to talk about it.

Her heart felt like stone. He hadn't sounded as if he meant it.

He was going to call the police from his house rather than hers, she saw when they pulled up in front of it a few moments later. When he saw her questioning glance, he said, "We'll be safer here." He hustled her up the sidewalk and put her inside the house with the same dispatch he had shown in their exit from the restaurant. He locked the door behind him and caught her arm. "Toni, look at me."

She tilted her face to his. Her heart was pounding, not with fear, with something else—some wild feeling as though she were standing on a precipice.

"Are you all right?"

His warmth and concern flowed over her like honey, filling her with a heat that chased away the shock. She made a choked sound and nodded her head. "You were in as much danger as I."

"Don't think about what could have happened. Nothing did. You're safe."

"But are you?" she blurted out, unable to contain her anxiety any longer. "It's you he's after, not me. Next time..."

He stood between her and the door as if to protect her from the outside world, and he was so close—close enough for her to feel his warmth and concern change to something hot and molten and explosive.

"What difference does that make to you?"

"That's right," she said sharply. "I forgot. I'm not supposed to care what happens to you. For all you know, I may have staged the whole thing." Filled with a bitter, aching regret and a cold that banished the warm feeling he'd given her a moment ago, she averted her eyes and half turned as if to step away from him.

Catching her arm and bringing her around to face him, he said in a cool voice, "If you planned the whole thing, why didn't you run when I told you to?"

She faced him defiantly, taut with pride. "Running wasn't in my plan."

"I don't believe you planned it. If you had, you wouldn't have saved me. Why did you save me? Why?" When she didn't answer, he said again fiercely, "Why, Toni?"

"Because I couldn't stand to see you there with that . . . that horrible glass next to your face—"

"Any more than I could stand seeing it next to yours. . . ."

Cay's mouth on her cheek was warm, and when he moved to her lips, his kiss shocked her with its depth and texture. His mouth was as sensual as spring rain and as thirst quenching. Yet she wanted more . . . and as if in answer to her instinctive need, he pressed closer, trapping her between his body and the wall.

She tried to remember how much he mistrusted and disliked her, but she couldn't remember a thing. She could only feel, and what she felt was wonderful.

"If he had touched you . . . if he had made one tiny mark on this satin skin of yours—" his tongue flicked out over her cheek "—I would have taken great pleasure in murdering him."

"Cay. . ."

His lips traveled the line of her jaw, down her throat and lower to the valley between her breasts. "So sweet. Lilac. It went deep inside my head that first night, and it won't go away."

He lifted his head and sought her mouth again, still holding her captive against the wall. A small protesting moan escaped her. Shifting slightly, he caught her leg between his thighs, and all the sensations that she'd felt earlier when her knee touched his thigh came back in a flood, intensified a thousand times.

"Cay, please, listen. I—"

"I don't want to listen, I don't want to talk. I want to kiss every inch of you and prove to myself that you're alive and well and unharmed." His mouth moved over her cheek. "I want to celebrate life with you in the oldest, most basic way. Come upstairs with me, sweetheart."

A husky male voice said, "Cay?"

The darkened hall was no longer a warm cocoon sheltering her with Cay. The world had intruded. A man stood a few feet away, the light from the living room playing over his face. "What are you doing here?"

"We came to spend the night. Toni, this is my manager, Morry Filmore. Morry, Toni Pereola."

Morry nodded at Toni, but his eyes were faintly derisive. He exuded disapproval from every part of his barrel-shaped body. Even the angle of the cigar clamped between his teeth spelled disdain. "What happened to bring you here?" He addressed the question to Cay, but his eyes lingered on Toni.

"Torgen came at us in a restaurant with a broken bottle. The only good thing about it was that he made a fool of himself in front of several witnesses. The bad thing is that after this little episode, I can't begin to guess what he'll do next. He used to stay inside the law. He's not restricting himself to that anymore. There's no way I can risk letting Toni go back to her house. She's staying here for the night. I'll put her in the room across from mine."

Morry's mouth twisted, and Toni's hands curled at her sides. She hardly knew the man, but he had certainly formed his opinion of her.

"The lady doesn't seem to have an overnight bag."

"I didn't want to stop at her house."

Cay was behind her, and Toni couldn't see him, but she could hear the flint in his voice. "I don't need to stay here," she said, looking at the man called Morry. "I can call Liz and ask her to come and then go home when she and Tommy get there."

She swung around to face Cay. Cay's eyes were dark, understanding and faintly self-mocking. "You'd rather be on your own turf, is that it?" he asked, giving a casual shrug. "All right, if that's what you want. But I'm going with you."

Morry grabbed his cigar out of his mouth and looked at Cay as if he'd taken leave of his senses. "Wait a minute. You're gonna go back over there with her and spend the night after what's happened?" He made a derisive sound, a half snort. "You told me yourself her house was a nightmare to secure, wide open to anyone who wanted to walk in. For God's sake—" he rounded on Toni "—show some sense. This house has electronic security... and a dead bolt on every door."

"With the surveillance I've set up at her house, we can manage," Cay said, his voice cool. "Morry, stop scaring the lady. She's had enough for one night."

Toni looked at the older man. "Is what you're saying true—about this house being safer?" She was thinking of Cay, not herself. She couldn't place him in danger again.

"Of course it's true," Morry snapped. "I don't talk just to hear my mouth flapping."

"Then I think perhaps we should stay here, for the night at least." She met Morry's eyes, fire in hers. "I won't place Mr. Sinclair in any more danger than he's already in."

"Toni, there's no need—"

"No, Mr. Filmore's right. We can't take any more chances."

It was an unexpected victory and achieved in an odd way, but Cay accepted the gift the gods gave and kept his face as smooth as glass.

Morry's eyes connected with Cay's, then swung to Toni again. She was pleased to see they had a faintly puzzled look in them. "You've obviously got more sense than he has. Manager is my honorary, face-saving title. I'm really the chief cook and bottle washer. Can I get you some coffee?"

It was an apology of sorts, but to Toni's ears, it lacked sincerity. "No, thank you. I don't think I could...drink anything."

"You've had a long day," Cay broke in. "Come upstairs and I'll show you your room." To Morry, he said, "I'll talk to you when I come back down."

Morry looked at Cay, his expression mocking and affectionate at the same time. "Sure. Breakfast is at eight, Miss Pereola."

"Please, don't go to any trouble for me. Just a cup of coffee is fine."

Morry was cool, polite. "I'm used to preparing breakfast for an occasional overnight guest of Cay's."

Morry couldn't have aimed the arrow more cannily, Toni thought, but she'd die before she'd let him see what a direct hit he'd scored.

She faced Morry, fighting to control her shaking knees. All the tensions of the night seemed to have suddenly rushed in. "I'm so glad to know I won't be any more of an inconvenience to you than Cay's other . . . guests have been."

Cay advanced a step on Morry and said in a firm tone, "That's enough."

Morry's cigar shifted to the other side of his mouth. "I've got just one thing to say to you. You've been coming to Key West for three years and this is the first time Torgen's found you here."

"This is the first time I've done a concert here."

"The same day you meet her . . . Torgen turns up." Morry stopped and took a breath, as if he had been running hard. "You think about that."

"I already have," Cay said dryly, his inflection telling Toni nothing. He led her away from Morry's animosity, up the stairs and into a bedroom done in shades of light blue and cream—a room that was blessedly neutral in gender. She looked around, hoping she wouldn't find a filmy negligee in one of the bureau drawers.

"There's never been another woman in this house," he said quietly.

She didn't move, didn't react. After a short pause, and still in a soft voice, he continued, "Now, as they say, the shoe is on the other foot. Isn't it? Do you believe what Morry said about my having frequent visitors?"

She swung around to face him. "I don't think you've ever brought a woman here before. That's why he's so worried."

Admiration brought the first light of amusement to his eyes that she had seen there during this long, tense evening. "Score one for the lady."

"I told you I'm not as quick to believe circumstantial evidence as you are."

"But perhaps I'll learn to be more trusting . . . if you go on giving me such superlative lessons. Don't, Toni."

"What did I do?"

"Your eyes went dark as if you were afraid of me as you were of Torgen earlier. Now that I have you up here, I'm not going to follow up on that kiss downstairs, if that's what you're thinking."

"I wasn't thinking that at all."

"Weren't you?" He sounded as cool and cynical as Morry had. "I knew you were off guard, and I took advantage of it." He turned on his heel and went out of the room, leaving her staring after him. Why had he left so abruptly?

She stood confused, aching, her brain vaguely registering the sound of a bureau drawer opening and closing in the distance.

Cay reappeared in the doorway as suddenly as he'd gone. His face devoid of expression, he came toward her and tossed a shirt and a new toothbrush on the bed. The shirt was silky purple with long sleeves and pearl buttons—probably something he'd worn on stage a million years ago.

"I don't have a spare pair of pajamas, I'm sorry."

Her eyes moved upward from his hands to his face. If Torgen had turned on him tonight and sliced his tanned skin or harmed his mouth, which had covered hers so skillfully...

"Surely the thought of wearing my shirt doesn't bother you that much."

"No." She turned away, not wanting him to guess what was really bothering her.

"Toni." He sounded strange, too controlled. "I have to make that call to the police. If you like, I'll send Morry up with some brandy."

"No, thank you. I . . . I'll be fine."

She stayed where she was, facing toward a window, waiting for the sound of the door closing. When she heard it, she knew he was gone—and he had taken part of her with him.

Now was the time. Now was the time to erect barriers—steel barriers. Now was the time to remember how little he trusted her and how very temporary a relationship with him would be.

It was not the time to recall how his hands had looked when he'd served her a slice of bread or how he'd moved to protect the small child or how he'd put her safety ahead of his own. Nor was it the time to remember how he'd sounded when he'd asked her downstairs in the darkened hall if she was all right or the way he'd said with a rough kind of desperation that he couldn't stand seeing her in danger.

It wasn't the time to admit that the barriers that she'd had around her heart for so long were crumbling bit by bit.

Plagued by a shaking restlessness that she told herself was a natural result of the evening's trauma, Toni showered in tepid water and put on the shirt that belonged to him. The silk smelled faintly of cedar, as if it had been stored and not worn for a long time. She repressed a mental image of Cay on stage wearing the garment she was putting next to her bare skin and concentrated on fastening the buttons down the front. The sleeves flopped over her wrists. She rolled first one and then the other up over her elbows. Conscious of the silk sliding over her breasts, she lay back in the bed, her eyes wide open.

Downstairs, Cay went to the phone and called the police, but when he finished talking he was angrier than before.

"The New York police couldn't pick him up because he didn't do anything illegal. Now even these guys are stalling." Cay slammed a fist against his knee.

"Why don't you ask your lady friend where he is?"

Gay turned slowly. Morry sat on the couch chewing on his cigar, a drink in his hand, his eyes old, watchful. Cay nodded at the glass. "Is that your liquid courage?"

"I don't need it to speak my mind to you."

"And now that she's safely out of the way, you're pulling out all the stops and saying what you've been dying to say since we walked in the door together, is that it?"

Faced with Cay's tightly controlled temper, Morry looked calm. "I didn't notice you doing much . . . walking. I must say I'm surprised. She isn't your usual fare."

Cay raised a dark eyebrow. "Maybe that's a point in her favor."

Morry shrugged. "She has a certain appeal—wide dark eyes to go with that nice, honest face—"

"Shut up, Morry," Cay said in a cool, clipped tone.

"Sure, Cay." Morry smiled and shifted his cigar, his eyes on his friend's face. "Should I stay downstairs tonight out of the way?"

"Go anywhere you damn well please as long as you stay out of my hair."

Morry's eyes narrowed. "Sure, Cay," he said again, far too casually.

Cay swore under his breath. This house had been his sanctuary for three years, but it wasn't now. With Morry sitting there looking like a damn cigar-smoking cat chewing on a canary, and Toni across the hall, it was going to be a long, long night. No matter where he went, his nerves would take a beating.

Swinging away from Morry's too-wise eyes, Cay said, "I'm going up. I'll see you in the morning."

"Sure you don't want a drink to relax your nerves?"

He did, but he wasn't going to have one. "No, I want a clear head just in case Torgen decides to drop by and finish what he started."

Cay went up the stairs and walked past the door to his studio, denying himself the release of playing the piano. Though the soundproofing in the room was good, it wasn't perfect, and he didn't want to disturb Toni. She'd been through enough tonight, and she needed sleep. He'd make do with a book.

Walking into his bedroom was like walking into a bowl of cream. Thick plush carpeting gave under his feet. The walls matched the rug exactly and so did the curtains that hung at the windows, which overlooked the second-story porch. Touches of purple stood out like beacons—purple pillows, a vase of silk violets on his huge chest of drawers. A sculpture fashioned as a mobile and composed of interlocking circles of purple and silver, which caught the light as they revolved and converged, hung over the head of his bed.

His bedroom was his cave, his retreat—the place where he locked intruders out and made his own world. He'd liked the designer's concept of making the room one color, but he had decided that the touches of royal purple were intended as a joke—a little pun on his status as a star.

You've walked in and out of this room for three years and never really looked at anything in it. Why are you looking at it tonight?

The answer danced in his mind. How would Toni look in this room?

Wonderful. She would look wonderful. She would make everything come alive. Against the cream spread, her dark skin and hair would have a pagan beauty.

Cay pulled his shirt over his head and dropped it on the floor. He needed a shower.

Toni lay in bed, listening to the small sounds that told her Cay had come up the stairs and gone into his room.

She heard the sympathetic clank of pipes in her bathroom and the hiss of running water in his, the water stopping, a drawer squeaking open and closed. Another muffled word came through the walls. Silence followed, a deep silence that was broken only by the sound of her thoughts.

SHE REMEMBERED THAT she'd gone to sleep with the light on. Now it was off, and she lay in a pool of silvered darkness. With a start, she realized someone was in the room.

"It's only me." Cay's voice drifted toward her from the direction of the window.

"What are you doing in here?" She felt confused, trapped between dreams and reality. His black hair caught the moonlight, but his face was shadowed.

"I'm making rounds, looking out your window, checking on you. This is the third time I've been in here. I didn't think I'd wake you. I'm sorry. Just go back to sleep. Everything is all right."

His black, moon-silvered head turned toward the window.

"You shouldn't be standing there. Someone outside could see you."

"That's exactly what I want them to do. If there's anyone out there, I want them to think I'm spending the night in this room."

The moonlight was a physical thing, playing over his hair, his bare chest, his jeaned legs, and spilling from the window down over her bed, picking out the shadow and substance of her under the light sheet. Or was it just that she was supremely conscious of her body?

"You don't need to stand guard over me—"

"Don't tell me what I need."

His voice made icy pools in the warm darkness.

Toni tried again. "I thought this house had a security system."

"It does. But security systems have been known to fail. I failed once this evening. I'm not in the mood to fail again."

"You didn't fail. You were . . . wonderful."

The dark, quiet form at the window didn't move. "No. You were wonderful. You risked your life for that child and then again for me."

"I wasn't in any danger."

The silence in the room echoed in her ears. "Weren't you?"

He'd misunderstood her. He thought she had inadvertently admitted her compliance.

"I meant I wasn't in danger because he isn't after me," she said in a low voice, an icy chill enclosing her heart. "It's you he wants to intimidate so you'll give him more money, not me."

Another long spell of quiet was her answer. He remained standing in the silvery light, not moving a muscle.

She couldn't stand his silence. "Do you believe me or have you been thinking about what Morry said?" She certainly had. She'd gone to sleep thinking about Morry and how his suspicions must have heightened Cay's.

"Should I be thinking about what Morry said?"

"It's only natural that you would. You know and trust him. You don't know me, and you trust me even less."

He muttered a sharp curse. It rang in her ears in the darkness, and the cutting, harsh sound wounded.

"What is it?"

"Stop being so damned . . . understanding."

"I'm sorry," she said in a frigid tone that told him she wasn't. "I do apologize."

Slowly he turned toward her. "I accuse you . . . and you say you can understand why I think the way I do." He shook his head. "I thought I knew everything there was to know about women. I thought I knew all their tricks, all their foibles, all their outer acts and inner lies. Then I met you . . . and I can't make you fit anywhere. You won't go into any box I know. You're either three times as clever as any woman I've ever known or you are exactly what you seem to be."

"You still suspect me." There in the darkness, it was easier to talk, knowing she didn't have to keep the pain from showing in her face, her eyes.

"Let's just say I've decided to keep a more open mind about you."

It wasn't enough. She stared at him for a moment. His face was becoming clearer now as her eyes became accustomed to the dark. "Would you please leave? I don't need you standing over me like a guard dog." She pulled the sheet up over her shoulder and rolled on her side, turning her back to him.

"I'll be back again in another hour," he returned in a dry tone. "I'll try not to wake you."

6

IT WAS THE HEAT that Toni was feeling, it had to be. It wasn't anxiety. She couldn't be anxious over meeting Sinclair simply because she hadn't seen him for twenty-four hours. It had to be the heat.

Sun and shade splashed over the sparse covering of grass on the lawn of Hemingway House, and cats played tag around the empty chairs that waited in readiness for the audience. A puss who was friendlier than most tried to curl up in the viola player's open case and was ejected with a firm but friendly hand. Another cat, the color of caramel, poked her inquisitive nose at Toni's open toe sandal and was told to go away and find lunch somewhere else.

The cat lifted startled green eyes to Toni—eyes that reminded her of Cay's. Had she imagined that gleam of anger in his when she'd walked out of his house yesterday morning and climbed into the van beside Liz? Had she imagined the rough edge of temper in his voice later that afternoon when she'd called to say she was staying in the house with Liz that night?

She'd hoped for a break from the unrelenting memory of him . . . and the feel of his mouth on hers. Out of sight had not been out of mind. He'd been inside her head since the moment she'd left him, and she'd waited to meet him this afternoon with equal parts trepidation and eagerness. Now, when it was time for him to put in an appearance at the concert, he seemed to have disappeared off the face of the earth.

She needed him. Everything was going wrong. The only thing she had done right all day was to decide to wear shorts and a halter to this ultraconservative gathering, where she knew most of the women would be in designer dresses. The temperature in the yard felt slightly under the boiling point. Her other decision, giving Liz the day off because there was so little equipment, had been a mistake. This "simple" concert had turned out to be not so simple. She'd had to park the van three blocks away and she'd already made two trips back to it. Not only that, she'd been here for an hour, setting up the bins and the mike, and she was hot and sticky and needed a shower. Where was Sinclair? If nothing else, she needed him to get the first violinist out of her hair.

Cerise was around thirty-five, a dark-skinned gypsy of a woman. The string player reminded Toni of the cat who'd sampled her feet. The woman held her head in the same high, proud way, used her eyes with the same bewitching ease and had the same sultry arrogance.

Cerise didn't look sultry at the moment. She looked irritated. She didn't like the way Toni had arranged the speakers and she absolutely refused to discuss the matter with anyone but Mr. Sinclair.

"How is it going?"

The deep, familiar voice coming from somewhere over Toni's shoulder had the immediate and confusing effect of sending her nerves into shock and filling her with joy. She covered her elation with irritation and whirled around. He, too, had opted for comfort. He wore white denim pants and a white cotton shirt and looked as cool as she felt hot. Work. She had to focus on work. "Oh, it's going great. The violinist hates everything I've done so far, and she's getting ready to hate anything I'll do the rest of the afternoon. She's snapped not one but two strings while she was tuning up, and I was elected to run all over this darned island looking for replacements. I don't recall that job being listed in my contract."

Cay raised an eyebrow and slanted her a look of congratulation. "Where did you find one?"

"I remembered that one of the Key West Association members is an amateur string player. We had a discussion about the acoustics of a Stradivarius violin over the phone one morning while we were talking about my taking this job. He was hoping I knew something about the work of some man who's trying to reproduce a Strad using scientific methods."

"And were your efforts appreciated?"

Toni closed her eyes. "Let's hope the woman's talent for Beethoven matches her flair for ordering people around. She also informed me that there's been a change in the program and the quartet will do a modern number that needs narration during the second half. She thought, as long as I was already here, there wouldn't be any problem with the microphone." Toni rolled her eyes heavenward. "I had to go back for the mixing board and set it up, and it will be a small miracle if I can keep the level adjusted correctly when I haven't heard the narration."

His eyelids dropped lazily over his eyes. "A change in the program should have been discussed with me."

"But you weren't here, were you?"

"Is that a veiled hint asking where I've been?"

"Take it any way you like."

"Like you, I was out . . . hunting." He spoke casually, and Toni's suspicions were immediately aroused.

Fear flared along her veins. "You were looking for Torgen."

He gazed at her and smiled in that way she was beginning to know well. "Did you find him?" she asked.

"No." His voice and face told her he wasn't going to answer any more questions. "Any problems other than broken strings?"

"She wants to discuss the setup with you."

"I've already discussed the setup with her on the phone. This is exactly the way she said she wanted it. Anything else?" When Toni didn't respond, he cast a casual eye over the porch at the arrangement of her equipment. "Why are you hiding your stuff behind a potted palm?"

"I was told to keep my 'obnoxious electronic noise-makers' out of sight while the quartet played and to bring the microphone out during the announcements and take it back afterward. She doesn't believe I can really turn the mike off back here at the board," Toni said dryly.

"Didn't you explain?"

"Why don't you do it? As producer, it's your job to keep everyone happy, not mine. She also said she needs more chairs."

"You think I can make her happy?" His eyes were alive with mocking amusement.

"I'm sure you'll do your best."

He stepped away from her and went toward the house. Within minutes he brought out folding chairs that he'd found heaven knew where, smiled charmingly at a heavyset woman with a floppy hat who'd come early as if for the sole purpose of standing under the banyan tree and scowling because she hadn't been allowed to sit down. Cay looked at her ticket and seated her with a flourish that would have pleased Sir Walter Raleigh. He leaned over and said something in the woman's ear and she laughed, her eyes bright with sudden good humor. Really it wasn't fair for one man to have all that charm.

With the same expediency, he set out two chairs in the back row and indicated that Toni should sit in the one beside him. A moment later, he was caught by Cerise.

Toni faded toward the banyan tree and far enough away that she couldn't hear what was being said. Unfortunately, she could still see them.

She had to admit the woman was good. She flirted with the greatest refinement. While she talked to Cay, the woman's eyes flashed fire, and her hands were as graceful as butterflies as they flitted through the air, occasionally coming to rest on her chest above her ample bosom. It was obvious she thought her music was the most important thing in the world. As she talked, Cerise gestured toward Toni, a scowl on her face.

In two minutes, Cay had her smiling.

As the time for the concert to begin approached, Cay took the violinist's hand and asked a question. She nodded and smiled. With a casual grace that came from working for years in front of the public, he walked with the woman between the row of chairs, which were now occupied, stepped up on the porch, and moved the microphone into position. After he had checked briefly to see that the rest of the quartet were ready, he introduced each of them, told the audience that their ability to blend their individual solo virtuosity into an ensemble was magic, and concluded with how thankful he was that the Key West Association was able to bring artists of such stature to the Keys. He paused, waited for the applause, bowed and walked off the porch.

His progress back down the grassy aisle toward Toni was accomplished with a soberly polite face, but once he had seated himself and the quartet began to play, his rogue's smile appeared.

"Thank God she has to keep that violin under her chin for the next twenty minutes or so. That woman can talk nonstop. I thought she was going to wear out my ears before I got a chance to hear her play."

"You looked as if you were enjoying it."

"Looks can be deceiving." He threw an arm around the back of her chair and sat so intimately close that the lady he'd seated earlier kept twisting around to look at them, her brows drawn together in a frown. Cay smiled back and cupped his fingers over Toni's shoulder.

Under the spell of the heat and the soaring music and Cay's touch, she felt lulled and dropped into another place, another time. She drifted in a fantasy world—a world where there was warmth and light and music that climbed and dipped and climbed again. . . .

"Stop looking so pensive," Cay murmured in her ear. "They'll think you don't like their music."

Her pensiveness had nothing to do with the music, but she couldn't tell Cay that. She could only sit with him in the dappled shade and feel the strength of the muscled arm that held her in a protective grip and know that it was all part of a fantasy. . . and nothing more.

When the quartet finished the Beethoven and stood to acknowledge the leaden, open-air sound of the applause, Toni stopped Cay with a hand on his arm. "It's my job," she told him in a low undertone. Cay shrugged and sat back in his chair while Toni moved forward.

On the porch, out of sight of the crowd, she reached for the mike. As soon as she lifted it, the crackle and pop in the amps told her she was in trouble. Behind her, the audience began to murmur and to Toni it seemed that the temperature on Hemingway's porch had just risen several degrees. She was angry—angry with herself because she'd been too relaxed, too certain that this concert was simple and wouldn't be fraught with the usual havoc that warm, moist air played with electrical connections, angry because she hadn't used her typical caution to forestall trouble.

Don't get emotional when you're working with electricity, her uncle's voice echoed in her ear. *It could cost you your life.*

Aware that she was standing on concrete, Toni set the microphone down carefully, but the hissing didn't stop. There was a loose connection somewhere, one live wire was touching another. Unless she found it, the noise would continue blurting out at random intervals until she corrected it or switched off the power. She pulled the connector at the mike head loose. Nothing wrong there. The problem must be at the other end, the connector that went into the amp.

Another loud pop exploded into the silence. A woman in the crowd tittered nervously. From around the corner, Cerise appeared, her face dark with anger.

"What is it?"

Just as suddenly as it started, the popping stopped. "A glitch," Toni told her.

Dark, well-shaped eyebrows went skyward. "What an unfortunate term. What exactly does it mean?"

"It's an intermittent problem. One that's difficult to pinpoint."

"Naturally it would be a problem that's difficult to pinpoint." She paused dramatically and then said with a faint sneer, "Do you by any chance have a pin?"

"Don't worry, Cerise," Cay said, suddenly appearing on the scene. "She'll get it fixed . . . if you stop badgering her."

Toni bent over the cord, tension gathering in her shoulders. She needed another connector, and she'd used her spare on the mike just this morning. In the last minute flurry of tracking down the violin string, she'd forgotten to pick up another one on her second trip to the van.

She straightened to face the irate woman with the violin under her arm. "Give me five minutes."

"Don't be ridiculous. I can't delay the concert that long. We'll do the narration without your broken speaker."

"No. The narrator won't be heard clearly above the strings," Cay put in coolly. "Do as she asks." Turning his back on the scowling woman, Cay said to Toni, "What do you need?"

"Another connector. I'll have to go back to the van and get one."

"I'll go with you and drive you back. That'll save time."

When Toni hesitated, Cay surmised she didn't want to accept his help, but in the end she did.

Together, they walked sedately past the crowd, but once they were outside the hedge, they broke into a running lope along the street. Toni was very aware of Cay beside her, adjusting his stride to match hers, running with relaxed, loose limbs.

Breathing fast, Toni skidded to a stop at the back of the van . . . and stared in surprised dismay. One of the rear doors was open a fraction of an inch.

"What's the matter?" Cay asked.

"I'm sure I locked that door. But it's not locked now."

Cay laid a restraining hand on her arm. A woman who was as much a perfectionist about the maintenance and care of her equipment as Toni wouldn't have left the door to her van unlocked. Someone had been there after her and jimmied the door open. And that someone could be inside the van, waiting.

Cautiously he moved around to the front and peered in. Toni came behind him. There was no dark figure huddled inside.

"Give me the key."

Again she hesitated.

"The key, Toni." He looked determined enough to wrestle it away from her. Reluctantly she handed it to him.

He tried the door on the driver's side. It was locked. He unlocked the door and swung into the driver's seat, twisting his head to look around.

There was no one in the back. Everything looked quite normal, and he was about to call himself a fool...when he saw a glass milk bottle propped against the rear door that they'd noticed was open. A string around the neck of the bottle was tied to the inside handle.

"What is it? What do you see?"

"I'm not sure." But he had a fair idea. A chill crawled over his skin. He slipped between the front seats and moved forward to take a closer look.

"Cay." Too late, he realized she'd followed him into the van and was sitting on the driver's seat on her knees.

"Shh. Don't move."

With exquisite care, not touching it, he bent over the bottle. Polished to a high sheen, the glass reflected the light in the shadowy van. Pale yellow crystals that looked as innocent as colored sugar filled the bottle to the brim. He knew what those crystals were—picric acid, a highly volatile chemical substance that exploded when it was bumped or jarred...the principle ingredient in TNT. If Toni had opened the door...

A hot anger swept through him, a fury like nothing he had ever known. If he ever saw Torgen again, he'd strangle him.

Through gritted teeth, Toni rasped, "What is it?"

"Picric acid, an explosive that detonates when jostled."

"Don't touch it. Cay, stay away from it."

"It's all right. Just sit very still and everything will be okay."

Scarcely breathing, she froze in the seat. "Oh, please . . . be careful."

She didn't have to ask him twice, he thought grimly, knowing he was a fool to let her stay in the van with him. But it was too late now. He couldn't tell her to get out. The slightest movement could jar the bottle and tip it over.

Because Toni was there behind him, he exercised every bit of control he had to forget his anger at Torgen and concentrate on the problem at hand. Her safety as well as his own depended on his ability to keep his head.

His insides tightening, Cay reached for a square of carpeting that lay within easy reach. With exquisite care and without touching the glass, he created a tube and wrapped it around the bottle. Perspiration beading his brow, he sat back on his heels and looked at his handiwork. The carpeting would cushion any jar or shock the bottle might receive. He could snap the string and lock the door and the whole business would be safe there until after the concert. Then he'd come back and neutralize it with water and report the incident to the police.

He twisted around to look at Toni. Her face was colorless.

"You look like you're going to faint. Take deep breaths and tell me where to find that connector you wanted."

The connector was exactly where Toni told him it would be.

"We can't drive back. Are you up to another run?"

She didn't reply.

"Toni." He pushed her ahead of him out of the van, eased the door shut, and ignoring the curious glances of a couple passing by on the street, he gathered her into his arms and held her gently, as if she were a child. "It's all right. Nothing happened." He caught her chin and tipped her head back. She closed her eyes and the warm sun beat down on her face, but it wasn't as warm as the heated skin where his fingers touched her. Everywhere else she was cold. She couldn't seem to stop shaking. Her knees wobbled, her hands trembled. "We should go back," she mumbled.

"I know," he agreed, but didn't let go of her. When at last he did release her, she turned away from him and began to walk rapidly down the street. He caught up with her, and filled with a need to release the whirling fear and shock, she broke into a run. But even as her feet pounded on the sidewalk, her mind replayed the scene over and over again. Cay bending over, Cay lifting the scrap of carpeting, Cay taking his life in his hands . . .

By the time they reached Hemingway House, Toni felt nauseated. It was Cay's hand on her elbow that steadied her and made it possible for her to walk through the crowd and go up on the porch. It was his presence that helped her control her shaking fingers enough to begin changing the connector. Still, in the process, she dropped the tiny screwdriver twice before she finally loosened the screws and wrapped the copper wire around them. Feeling fractionally calmer, she finished the task and stood up. Cay's hand came to rest on her shoulder.

"Good work," he whispered.

She swayed, the heat and shock making her feel light-headed. Cay's hand went around her waist to support her.

Cerise's eyes flickered over Cay's supporting arm. "I presume the microphone is operable."

As the other woman's cool, speculative gaze swept over them, Toni felt the muscles in Cay's body tighten. "It's all yours," Cay told her.

Cerise smiled in a show of mocking politeness and said, "If you are ready, then."

Toni stepped away from Cay and forced herself to pick up the mike and follow the violinist. The ampli-fier and microphone were functioning beautifully, and Cerise's explanation about her regret for the delay and the change in the program could be heard clearly.

The world would not stay right side up. Cay grabbed her arm. "Steady. You've had a shock."

"You do have a talent for understatement. You might have been killed."

Cay studied Toni's face, wondering how much that thought really bothered her. "No. It was planned so that the bottle would drop to the cement just as whoever opened the door was looking down. I would have been disfigured, not killed."

His eyes were quiet, watchful. Then it hit her. "You...you can't think I had anything to do with this."

"It doesn't seem likely."

It doesn't seem likely.

All through the rest of the concert, while Toni forced her mind and fingers and ears to work in a coordinated effort, mixing the sound for the narration, Cay's words went round in her head like a ballerina in a child's music box. Her mood had not improved when the concert ended and they returned to the van, defused the lethal package by dousing it with water, delivered it to the police and answered their questions. Outside the police station, Cay walked her to the van and said, "Where would you like to have dinner?"

She stared straight ahead of her. It was dusk and the streets were darkening.

"Why didn't you tell the police about me?"

Cay wore his smooth, unreadable public face. "I didn't think there was anything to tell. You told me there wasn't." She turned away, but he caught her arm. "You didn't answer my question about dinner."

Looking up at him with a quicksilver gaze that came straight from her heart, she said, "You didn't answer mine." She stood where she was, conscious of the way he was holding her wrist tightly but not too tightly. She could walk away if she wanted to. She didn't want to.

"You say you want my complete trust. Let me ask you this, Toni. Do I have yours?"

"I . . . don't know what you mean."

"Suppose I said that I trusted you completely. Where would we go from there?"

His dark eyes told her quite clearly where he wanted her to go with him.

"Now you seem to be having trouble answering my question," he said quietly.

She tried to think. She could say she still didn't know what he meant, but it would be a lie. She knew exactly what he meant. Every minute spent in his company heightened her awareness of him. Now, with her nerves still taut from shock, his dark attraction was more compelling than ever. How easy it would be to say yes to his question. How hard it would be to leave him when her work in Key West was finished. "I'd like to have dinner somewhere quiet," she said finally. "A place where we wouldn't have to worry about being accosted."

For a moment, she thought he wasn't going to allow her to change the subject. Then slowly he let go of her wrist. "That sounds like an excellent idea. I think I know just the place."

INSIDE THE WALLED and shaded privacy of Cay's garden, Toni reclined on one side of the blanket, propped on her elbow, a piña colada in her hand. Cay lay sprawled like a lazy cat across from her. Only the remains of their meal lay between them, and as if he'd read her thoughts, Cay sat up and began to clear the paper bags and white cartons away.

She hadn't been hungry when she'd walked into the garden, but the spicy Mexican tamales and fritos Cay had bought from the little sidewalk café had teased her appetite back. She'd eaten and enjoyed it all, but the tangy food had made her thirsty. Now, some whisper of caution in her mind was telling her she was enjoying the fruity taste of the pineapple and coconut drink too much, but she quieted that disturbing thought by telling herself she would sip this one.

Cay had said little during dinner. She hadn't felt like talking, either. She'd wanted to let the peace and quiet of Cay's sanctuary seep into her soul. She suspected that his bringing her here was a privilege he accorded few people. A man who had learned to savor his privacy did not relinquish it easily.

The garden was the best of two worlds—tropical and wildly overgrown around its boundary and neatly landscaped within. Palms sheltered them on three sides. The house protected them on the fourth. Red hibiscus grew in profusion beside purple bougainvillea. Water lilies as white as a swan's neck floated on the surface of a small pool. The fountain swooshed and splashed, and palm fronds rustled overhead. A bird warbled a late-evening song, and under Toni, the grass was as plush as a carpet. The mingled perfume of hibiscus and roses drifted in the air like the scent of wine . . . and was as intoxicating.

Cay's eyes traveled down the length of her bare legs. "Are you getting cold?"

"No." She wasn't cold at all. She felt pleasantly warm inside and out, and so relaxed.

Her elbow slackened and she flopped on her back and looked up at the sky. It was peach. A peach sky. How strange. People believed the sky was blue, but it wasn't at all. It was really a gorgeous peach color. It only masqueraded as a blue sky during the day to fool the populace, and Toni told Cay so.

Cay told himself he must have an unscrupulous streak. He hadn't intended to let Toni drink too much, but when she'd asked for her third refill from the pitcher Morry had mixed, he hadn't refused. Now she lay on her back, her slim, tanned body a delectable dish that he'd like to have for dessert, her shining black hair inviting him to touch.

Suffer, Sinclair. It's your own damn fault for not limiting her alcoholic intake. Those who sin against the innocent will be punished.

Was she innocent? Dammit, was she?

How could she be anything else, looking the way she did?

Looks can be deceiving.

"I thought flowers didn't like rock music."

"What?" Cay lay down on his stomach next to her, keeping a careful three inches away, but treating himself to a full view of her face.

She gestured toward the flowers that dangled from the high walls he'd had built around the garden. "I read somewhere that plants don't like rock music."

"I'll be very careful to close all the doors and windows when I practice." He smiled down at her. "Nice of you to worry about my flowers."

"I worry about everybody's flowers. They're the only flowers I have. I'm on the road too much to have my own, so I try to love other people's as much as I can."

A lazy fingertip probed the tiny wrinkle that had started to form between her brows. "You can love my flowers any time you want to," he murmured.

She sighed and snuggled her head into the blanket in pure contentment. "Cay, it's so beautiful here. Look at that one hibiscus. It looks as if it's not attached to anything; it's just floating in thin air. That's the way I feel."

"Is it?" He looked down at the satin smoothness of her skin, the dark aliveness of her black hair. She looked pagan, utterly relaxed and utterly desirable. "I feel a little like I'm free-falling myself." Her mouth looked delectable. He had to taste it. . . .

Toni looked up and saw the lean lines of his face coming closer and closer. She said, "Did your parents ever tell you about the birds and the bees?"

He stopped dead and hovered over her, gazing down into her clear silver-gray eyes, caught between a faint urge to strangle her, the impulse to laugh and a fierce need to kiss her. She looked deadly serious, completely sincere. How much had she had to drink? "They didn't have to," he replied, struggling to be as serious as she. "I was raised on a ranch."

"Mine didn't, either. I was just trying to remember whether it's the stamen or the pistil that carries the seed."

"There's a gap in your education. Maybe it's those two years of college you missed. Why did you miss them, Toni? You're not a quitter."

She went as tense as if he'd struck her. He looked down at her eyes and saw only a mirror of his own. "It's a long and boring story. You wouldn't want to hear it. . . ."

Her reaction piqued his interest. He'd been curious about why she'd left college since she'd mentioned it the first night, when they'd dined together. Now he was more curious than ever. "Tell me," he urged. "Or I'm going to kiss you . . . no matter what outrageous thing you say this time."

Her eyes widened slightly at his perception.

"Umm," he murmured, "you're half out of it, but you still have enough wits left to dodge a kiss you don't want."

"It isn't that I don't want you to kiss me. It's just . . ."

"Then tell me your life story, Toni Pereola."

"No, I can't. Cay, please don't—" His mouth brushed over her face and her ability to think two coherent thoughts in a row vanished. The light nibbling of his teasing lips brought a startling tingle to her skin as if her blood had suddenly remembered how to flow. Her hands reached out and slipped under his arms, finding the heated warmth of his body. He tasted her cheeks and her eyelids, the lobe of her ear, the sensitive skin at her temple.

"Tell me what I want to know," he said huskily.

"No." He meted out her punishment; the curve of her cheekbone received loving attention, his lips claiming it with a gentle, suckling possession. "Cay, please . . ."

Her throaty whisper held the longing he'd wanted to hear for so long. "I'm right here, sweet. Oh, God, so sweet—"

Her eyes were as filled with passion as he wanted them to be. Her breathing was shallow, and her throat glowed with a rosy satin that betrayed her readiness to be loved. She was aroused, as aroused as he was. So lovely. So responsive. So ready to give.

And it was all wrong. He didn't want to take. Cay wanted to give, as well—give her all that he was, or would be. Seeing her like this, her inhibitions lowered by the drinks he'd let her have, her hair tousled like a child's, he was filled with a fierce need to protect her from anything that might harm her, including his own hunger.

He rolled away from her and sat up, leaning his head forward on his knees, fighting to regain control of his body.

Instantly concerned, she came up beside him, her breast accidently brushing his bare arm. "Cay, I—"

Muttering a word, he got to his feet. "I think you'd better go inside and sleep this off."

She didn't move. He gathered her up in his arms and felt his body leap. God, in another three minutes, he'd be paying royally for his chivalrous bent.

She didn't tense when he stood up with her. She lay as relaxed in his arms as a kitten, the pupils of her eyes slightly dilated.

Toni felt him bearing her into the house and up the stairs with a ridiculous ease that spoke of strength not yet used. She shouldn't let him do this. She should protest, say something. Her mouth felt drugged with the need for the kiss he'd hadn't given her, and her eyes weren't focusing on anything except the bridge of his nose. He had such a sleek, aristocratic nose. She'd thought so, right from the first night she saw him. Did he know what a nice nose he had?

She asked him. A half smile twitched the corner of his mouth. He had a nice mouth, too. Did he know that?

He seemed to go tense suddenly, his hands tightening around her body. He must think her a pest with all her questions. Yes, that was it, he thought she was a pest and he was letting her go.

He must be letting her go, because she couldn't feel the warmth of his body or his hands, and his mouth and nose were no longer close to hers. She was floating on something that was soft as an angel's cloud. It was the ocean. There seemed to be waves. . . .

Cay looked down at her. He'd lifted the spread out from under her, and now she lay on his water bed on her side, her knees curled, her eyes closed. He should have taken her to her own room. Why hadn't he?

Because he wanted her close. When the effect of the liquor wore off, Toni might wake and need him. If she was in her own room, she'd never come into his. The only way to be sure she slept through the night without having bad dreams was to keep her here.

Muttering a succinct word under his breath, Cay decided he wasn't masochistic enough to subject himself to the punishment of undressing her. She could sleep in her halter and shorts. He lifted her legs and tucked them under the light sheet and pulled it up over her shoulders. Casting a dark look at the couch, he decided he wasn't masochistic enough to subject himself to that couch, either. It was too short and he'd have a stiff neck in the morning. His bed was huge. He'd manage to stay on his own side, probably better than she would.

7

TONI'S EYES FLEW OPEN, and in the predawn light of the room, lying on her stomach, she saw cream sheets, not blue ones. She knew instantly where she was. And there was no mistaking the hard masculine hip and thigh butted against hers. "What am I doing here?"

From just under her elbow, a husky male voice groaned, "You're doing what you do best. Hogging the bed."

His warm breath fanned her elbow. She was on her stomach, cuddled against him, her arm in his face. "I'm sorry," she said instantly, trying to move away from him. With an arm circling her bare waist, he captured her and brought her back against him, fitting her body spoon-fashion into his.

"Don't move. You're fine." He tried not to think about how fine she was.

"Cay—" Warm, bare male legs, covered with crisp hair and hard with muscles, tangled with hers. He wasn't naked, but he was very close to it. Along her back she felt the bareness of his chest and the firm hardness of his abdomen.

He stroked her hair. "How are you feeling?"

How was she feeling? What a question. She felt like a woman...in a way she'd never felt before. "I...have a headache."

"I'll get you some aspirin."

"No—" She didn't want him to move.

"Don't be an idiot." The warmth of his hands and body left her. His dark form moved across the floor. The bathroom light clicked on, showing his lithe body clad in a pair of briefs. She was awake now and aware of the pain that pounded at her temples . . . and of the heat that stirred in a lower region.

"Here." He gave her two tablets, and with his help and support, she sat up and swallowed them with the water he'd brought.

He left her, but the light from the bathroom revealed the easy grace of his almost bare body moving away from her in far too much detail. He returned and placed a cool cloth on her forehead. "I shouldn't have let you drink so much."

"I'm a grown woman. I knew what I was doing."

The tone of her voice alerted him. She meant what she was saying. "Did you?" He sat back slightly to look at her face in the faint light. "Well? What were you doing?" He sounded curious and faintly amused.

"I was trying to . . . forget."

"Forget what happened?"

"No. Forget what . . . what you think of me."

"I told you it doesn't make any difference what I believe."

"It does to me," she replied.

"So you can keep me at a distance?"

"I don't seem to be at a distance from you now." She peered at him from under the cloth on her head. Her silver eyes entranced him.

All the feelings that had been held so long at bay came rushing up within her. She remembered his fierce protectiveness in the restaurant when Torgen had threatened her and his unwillingness to leave her. And last night . . . last night he could have made love to her. She had drunk too much, but not enough to be unaware of him, of the tender way he'd carried her up the stairs or of the way he'd laid her in his bed and made no demands on her. And now he was caring for her again, seeing to her needs and ignoring his own.

She'd fought the attraction he had for her. She'd been unconsciously fighting it for five years—from the first night, when she saw him playing in concert, until last night, when he was lying stretched out next to her like a lazy panther. She'd fought . . . and lost the battle.

"Toni, don't look at me like that," he said softly. "You're encouraging me to take unfair advantage of you."

"I know," she answered, surprising him.

"I've been rather heroic on a couple of different occasions, but I think this well of chivalry you've tapped is fast running dry."

"Cay." She slid her hands up his bare chest. "Stop being so . . . chivalrous."

She kept her hands on his chest as he bent to turn on a small lamp sitting on a table by the bed. Soft light bathed the room, gleamed off the mirror on his dresser and left the huge circular bed in shadows.

"You *are* awake, aren't you?" he murmured.

"Yes, I'm awake."

"And in full command of your faculties."

Her fingertips played over his biceps. "Now that, I'm not all together sure about."

She couldn't read the look in his eyes, but there was a tension in his body and a sudden shifting of his weight that made the bed ripple. Shivering sensations of pleasure shot up from the base of her spine.

He leaned forward and gathered her up into his arms. "Toni." It was just her name, but breathed in such a husky, strained, way that she trembled.

Gently releasing her, he lay down beside her and watched her as he stroked her shoulder lightly. Lost in the pleasure he created, she closed her eyes.

Under her, the water rippled gently, echoing the motion of his hands. His palms slid under her spine, and her halter loosened.

Warm lips came to feast on the flesh he had bared, exploring, nuzzling around the string, tickling, tugging, while his silky hair brushed her skin.

He set the bed in motion and the halter vanished. Her neck and shoulders and her breasts were bare—a satiny expanse of smooth flesh under the curve of her throat. A cool breeze wafted over her. "Cay, please—"

"Toni." His voice was dark, commanding. "Lie back and relax."

She couldn't. She seemed to be filled to overflowing with ecstasy. The gentle rocking of the bed combined with his caress... He fitted her breasts in his hands possessively. He had never touched them before, but they swelled to his touch as if they had always been his.

His thumbs created a new ache deep within her. She arched to him, her body instinctively seeking his, her mind reeling with the heady pleasure he created. Watching her, he went on caressing her, making her body throb with a sweet, slow drugging torture.

When the pleasure became too intense, she closed her eyes. Then she felt his hair brush her as he leaned over and explored the slope of her shoulder with his tongue.

Just as she was sure that she could no longer bear having anything between his hands and her body, he turned his attention to the fastener at her waist.

She would have turned, but he caught her by the hip and held her in place, trailing a careless finger from throat to navel. His mouth followed, pressing kisses. She hadn't known there were nerves under her breastbone that were so erotically sensitive.

When he had finished kissing her, she lay nude before him with even the final wisp of covering gone. His eyes, darkly possessive, roved over the creamy perfection of her skin. She looked at him anxiously. "I'm not . . . tanned all over."

He sat very still, as if he were trying to control some emotion he didn't want her to see. "Yes," he said, his voice muffled, "I can see that." And he proceeded to explore the places that weren't tanned all over.

"Do you . . . mind?"

"Yes." He kissed her eyes as she looked up in startled dismay. "And I intend to spend several days in my garden with you remedying your shameful condition. Will you sunbathe in the nude with me, sweetheart?"

He didn't wait for her answer. He plucked her hands from her sides and said, "Touch me, Toni. God, I've waited so long for this...."

With her eyes gleaming like silver, she flattened her palms on his chest. His evenly tanned shoulders offered masculine curves to tantalize her fingers. She ran her hands over him, savoring the delights of his hair-roughened skin and its underlying musculature.

She discovered his tight male nipples, which were half hidden in a nest of dark hair. She explored one of the intriguing nubs and felt it harden under her fingers. His response pleased her and sent a shiver of reaction along her skin. Impulsively she leaned forward and ran her tongue over the tight bud.

"You," he breathed, "are an unscrupulous woman quite undeterred by the quality of mercy."

"Does that mean you like what I do to you?"

"It means I like it far too much."

He stood up and stripped away the one garment he wore. He was as graceful as she had imagined, yet there was power in his sleek muscles. Male, primitive, he came down on the bed, rocking it with his weight, gathering her into his arms.

Lying down beside her, he ran his hands over her, exploring the curve of a thigh, soothing and exciting her at the same time.

The beauty of his lean face matched the grace of his body. He was whole, sure of himself, and yet, as he held her and gazed at her, there was a stillness about him as if in these last moments he were giving her the chance to change her mind. She could only guess at the strength of his control that made his waiting possible.

Love swept through her, destroying every vestige of doubt. She turned to him and clasped her arms around his waist.

Looking humble and yet ecstatic, he held her in his warm grip and wriggled his hips, making the bed undulate. Pulling her close, he leaned over to gently lay himself half over her softness. "You feel like heaven. Sheer heaven."

While her head reeled with his husky words, he began to kiss her in places she hadn't known could come to life with such fiery warmth—the hollow below her shoulder bone, the inside of her arm, her flattened abdomen. He explored and claimed new territory for his own, trailing his lips over her hipbone, down the length of her slender thigh, over the sensitive crown of her knee. And while his mouth tasted her, his hands sought and found the treasure, that part of her that ached for his possession.

Her body surged with new and heady delights. Cay held her tenderly, soothing her with kisses, driving her wild with caresses. He touched her gently, touched her passionately, possessed her and gave her the freedom to soar.

Through a haze of love and desire, her fingers sought and found him, tracing a line of sleek skin and muscle, brushing a hair-roughened thigh.

Naked, beautiful to her eyes, he prolonged the sweetness, leaning over her to kiss her breast. Silken hair brushed her skin. In a torment of need, she murmured his name.

"Ah, sweet. I'm strongly tempted to make you wait, but I can't—" In a lower, agonized whisper, he said again, "I can't."

He moved and so did she, and the imaginings of her dreams were nothing compared to the reality of the low, sweet slide of his body into hers. They were together, complete, one. Toni was filled with an aching bitter-sweetness, a soaring ecstasy...and a sudden need to cry.

Moments later, Cay lifted away, looked down into her face and saw at once the conflicting emotions mirrored there.

"Giving up your loneliness doesn't always come easily to you, does it, Toni?"

Cay kissed her lightly on the nose, a devilish gleam of amusement in his eyes, and rolled, taking her with him. Settling her on top of him, he smiled up into her face. "More comfortable now?"

"Cay..." He was so perceptive, so understanding, so willing to subject his male pride and power to her needs, that love for him swept through her like an avalanche, overwhelming her. To hide the love she knew was shining from her eyes like a beacon, she buried her head in his shoulder.

"You are more comfortable, aren't you?" He sounded anxious, worried by her stillness and silence. His hands traveled over her back, soothing, entreating.

Toni lay still for a moment longer, unable to move. Then, with her eyes moist with emotion and full of mischief, she executed a shifting motion with her hips that made his breath catch in his throat. "I'm fine," she taunted him lightly. "How about you?"

"Oh, I'm better. So much better..." He brought her head down to his and showed her exactly how much with a kiss that pulsed and throbbed with his pleasure. The sensual exploration of his tongue told her the time of teasing was over. He was her lover now, a man intent on loving her with all the strength and grace and skill at his command. His body was no longer a mystery to her, nor was hers to him; and yet there was a deeper mystery, the mystery of how, joined with him, they created a force stronger than both of them.

He gave her heaven, and she was desperate to give him just as much, until the giving dissolved into a molten heat that brought his name to her lips....

TONI AWOKE IN A ROOM golden with sunlight. She was lying on her stomach, and Cay was nibbling around the edges of her elbow.

"Have you thought of having this instrument of death registered with the police department?"

"I'm sorry." Her voice was fuzzy with sleep, her body languorous with love. "Did I hurt you?"

"Yes."

Awake and instantly concerned, she balanced herself on her much-maligned elbow and looked at him. His dark beauty drew her eyes and filled her with pleasure. "Where?"

"Everywhere." He grabbed her upper arms and pulled her half on top of him so her breasts brushed pleasantly against his chest. "Will you kiss and make it better?" he said throatily.

"Idiot." Her epithet bounced harmlessly off him. Lying there, he looked utterly pleased with himself, a picture of masculine satisfaction. Her heart full to bursting with love for him, she had to lean down and brush her lips over his.

When she lifted away to look at him, he reached up and traced a finger down a satin strand of her dark hair to the end that curled under her chin. "Is that any way to talk to your lover?" His voice was husky, richly masculine. His eyes fastened on hers. "I am your lover, Toni."

Her hesitation was slight, but it was there. "Yes. I know."

Carelessly, he trailed a finger lower, to rest on the curve of her breast. "We could go down and make breakfast together. Are you hungry?"

He was filled with a primitive need to claim her again, to make love to her so thoroughly that she would never be able to deny the rightness of their being together.

"Yes."

"For food?"

She didn't hesitate. "No." Looking delighted by her truthfulness, Cay brought her head down to receive the kiss that was waiting for her on his mouth.

CAY LAY AWAKE, staring into the morning light. The music played in his head in a rare, priceless whole. The melody and chord progressions were complete. If he didn't get up and write it down now, the music would vanish from his mind like a wisp of smoke.

Beside him, her face bathed in the golden glow of the dawn, Toni lay on her stomach, her head propped on her hands and her elbows out. She slept like a child, the sheet pulled across her shoulders. An aching tenderness spread through him. He longed to reach out and stroke her dark hair, which was rumpled from their lovemaking. Knowing it would be cruel to wake her from such a deep, restful sleep, he resisted his need to touch her. Instead, he slid out of the bed and silently reached for his underwear.

He'd had the music room partially soundproofed the first year he'd bought the house, more because he wanted privacy than out of any consideration for his neighbors. Now, he was glad for the acoustical tile that would keep the sound of his piano from waking the woman who slept in his bed in the next room.

He sat down at the piano and picked out the melody and the chords he had heard in his head. The song flowed effortlessly from his fingers, as if he were playing it for the hundredth time, not the first. He ran through it once and then sorted through the pile of manuscript paper on the piano to find a blank sheet.

In an hour, using chord symbols, he had it all down. He stopped playing and flexed his shoulders, suddenly aware that the sun was blazing into the room, filling it with midmorning light. He felt her presence even before he saw her.

"It's lovely."

Bracing himself and wondering what her state of mind would be, Cay looked up. Dressed in a robe he'd forgotten he had, a light gray silky one that came to her knees, she stood in front of the open door, leaning against the frame. "Do you like the music?" he said casually, still uncertain of her mood.

"Yes, very much. Does it have words?"

"Not yet." Over the top of the piano, he studied her. "Are you holding up the door?"

Toni shook her head. "It's the other way around. The door is holding me up."

"You feel in need of support this morning?" He waited. There was a peculiar sensation of pressure in his chest.

"Not support exactly." She lifted her head. "It's just that I . . . didn't like waking up alone."

He stayed where he was at the piano, but it took all his willpower to do so. He wanted to go to her and gather her up in his arms and kiss her breathless to reward her for her honesty. But he couldn't. She'd taken her first step toward him, and he wanted her to take another. "There's a simple solution to that problem."

"There is?"

"Come live with me."

He expected her instant refusal. Instead, she stood silent, and at last, she breathed the words, "I can't."

"Why not?" he asked coolly.

"Cay, I—" She stopped and her eyes moved down over his bare chest. The rest of him was hidden by the piano. "Do you always practice with next to nothing on?"

"Not always. Sometimes I don't bother with the 'next to nothing.'" He winked at her and she glowered back at him. Her irritation pleased him. "Besides, I like to be comfortable when I'm composing, and I didn't think you'd wander in here. I thought you'd sleep through, and I'd come back to the room and dress before you woke." He grinned lazily at her, letting her think she'd succeeded in distracting him from a serious discussion about her future with him.

"It's a good thing you've got a padded bench. Otherwise, you'd stick to it."

He raised a quizzical eyebrow and gazed at her over the top of the piano. "What do you know about sticky piano benches?"

"I spent an hour a day for three miserable years on them."

"With all that time at a keyboard, you must be able to play something. Come and show me."

"What would you like to hear? 'Chopsticks' or 'Heart and Soul'?"

He winced. "That's the sum total of your repertoire?"

"That's it. And you have to play the left hand because I only know the right hand part."

"Well, what are you waiting for?"

"Waiting for?"

"You can't play the piano from over there."

"You don't really want to hear 'Chopsticks.'"

"Are you coming," he asked in a silky voice, "or shall I come and get you?"

She stood unmoving. "It's not going to work, you know."

"What isn't going to work?"

"All that marvelous professional tolerance mixed with your equally devastating sexual magnetism."

"I'm only asking you to play 'Chopsticks' with me. Anything else can wait until after we've had breakfast." He smiled a heart-melting smile. "What trouble can we get into sitting on a piano bench?"

"That all depends on what trouble you had in mind."

"It isn't trouble I have on my mind. I am thinking of you." He smiled at her blandly. "On second thought, that's trouble. Are you going to come over here?" When she didn't move, he said softly, "I dare you."

In a daze, she moved toward him. The thought that he was beginning to know her far too well drifted about the periphery of her mind. If he'd ordered her to come to him, she would have defied him. "You'll regret it."

He didn't seem to. She walked around the bench to the upper end of the keyboard and she sat down next to him, brushing his bare thigh with her silken-clad one. "Maybe we ought to have one good-morning kiss to start things rolling," he said. Pulling her around into his arms, he captured her mouth with his. He'd caught her by surprise, and her lips were already parted as if she'd been about to say something. He thrust his tongue into that waiting sweetness and savored the soft moan that came from her throat and the feel of her slender body under the silk.

When he finally released her, she looked flushed. "Feeling more awake now?" He gently cupped her breast.

She looked dazed. "Unless you want to continue what you just started, you'd better put your hands on the piano, Sinclair."

His laugh pleased her. Still chuckling, Cay dropped his hands and fit them over the keys.

He played the four-bar introduction alone. At his signal, Toni plunged in and stumbled through the first few bars. As the music progressed, she got into the spirit of the thing, executing sweeping glissandos that started at the top of the keyboard and ended inelegantly when her fingers crashed into Cay's at the bottom. Just as they were a few measures from the grand finale, the door opened.

Morry, clad in jeans and a loose shirt, stood in the doorway. "What the hell is that noise?"

"We were . . . playing," Cay replied in a dry tone.

Morry's eyes moved from Cay's bare chest to Toni's disheveled hair and the silken robe that hung slightly open at her neck. "So I see." His tone was just as dry. "Officer Clarke from the police department is on the phone. He wants to talk to you."

Cay opened his mouth as if he were going to protest. Then he shook his head, turned to Toni and adjusted the sides of the robe at her throat, pulling them closer together. "Don't go away, Liberace. I'll be right back. Morry, how about rustling up some breakfast for us?"

Confident that he had sent Morry on his way, Cay walked out of the room.

Toni rose from the piano and stood up to go back to the bedroom and dress . . . and found Morry blocking her path.

"You and I need to talk."

"What about?" She lifted her chin and faced him squarely.

"About you and Cay."

He was staring at her as if he'd like to give her the third degree and was wondering how to do it. "He won't give you one red cent."

"How can you be sure of that?"

Morry's eyes glittered with triumph. "I'll see to it that he doesn't."

Toni stepped forward. Before he could move away, she gripped his arm, leaned over and kissed him on the nose. "That's awfully sweet of you." She savored the startled look in his eyes for a moment, then slid past him and went to the door. Her fingers on the frame, she turned and said in a honeyed tone, "Has anyone ever told you you're wonderful?" She left him standing there with a shell-shocked expression on his face that pleased her immensely.

A few minutes later, Cay swept back into the bedroom. Toni was standing there, still wearing Cay's robe and wondering if she could take a shower without Cay thinking she had accepted his offer to move in. "All right," he said. "I want to know what happened."

"Nothing happened," she told him serenely.

His eyebrows shot up in disbelief. "Nothing happened?" He took a menacing step closer. "Don't tell me fairy tales, lady. Morry is stomping around the kitchen like a bear with a sore paw. I come up here expecting to find you dressed and gone and instead you're still here and still wearing my robe with an expression on your face that would flatter the Queen of Sheba. What did he say to you?"

Cay looked tense, grim. She asked, "Did the police find Torgen?"

"No. Now answer my question."

"Morry told me I'd never get any money out of you."

Cay stood several feet away from her, but in the bright morning light, she could see his almost nude body hardening with tension. "And what did you say to him?"

"I didn't say anything."

Another step brought him closer yet. "You must have said something."

"Well, now that you mention it, I do remember telling him I thought he was sweet and wonderful. That was after I kissed him." She raised her eyes, which were full of laughter, to him.

Cay stood for a moment, looking at her.

She let her eyes travel down over his lean, scantily clad body. "Didn't anyone ever tell you it's quite indecent to walk around the house wearing so little?"

"You kissed him?"

"Yes, I did, actually." He stepped closer and she tilted her head up to him, her smile full of impish mischief. "Are you jealous?"

"I don't believe it," he breathed. "To my knowledge, no one has ever bested Morry in a fight. No one. And to think you did it in a discussion of something you're as sensitive about as money—" He smiled an ecstatic, blazing smile at her. "Toni. Toni." The last was a shout of joy, a cry of relief. He wrapped his arms around her waist, lifted her off the floor and whirled her around with him.

"Cay, put me down. Cay—"

"Never," he cried. "Never."

"I need a shower. Put me down you idiot. Cay!" Her startled exclamation came as he lifted her off her feet and carried her into the bathroom. "Cay—"

He stopped her protest with a kiss and stripped her robe away. Once in the shower, he cleansed her, treasured her and worshipped her. Impatient to return pleasure for pleasure, she did the same, learning how sensitive his back was and how much he enjoyed having her touch him anywhere she cared to. He stood under the water and gave her yet another gift, the gift of his unselfconscious response to her caresses. When he finally groaned and drew her under the gentle downpour of water with him to give her a kiss that drew her soul from her body, she knew that he had given her more than she could ever repay him in a lifetime of loving. It was then that she knew she had to stay with him until she left Key West. This would be an interlude, a time snatched away from reality.

When she made the decision to allow herself two and a half weeks of heaven, the final wonderful moments of their shower and the sleek feel of Cay's cooled body as he drew her down on the bed and began to make love to her filled Toni with bittersweet happiness. His touches, his kisses, his murmured words of admiration and praise were tiny jewels to be tucked away in her memory and savored when she was no longer able to lie in Cay's arms.

She managed to act normally as they rose and dressed and talked about how starved they were, but underneath, a current of sadness ran through her.

In the afternoon they decided to risk the possibility of another encounter with Torgen and went to the beach. Cay stretched out on one of the huge beach towels he'd brought, and she sat down next to him. With the sun beating down on his lean body, he relaxed and his eyes closed in drowsiness.

Toni, too, felt sleepy, drugged with warmth and love. There was a peacefulness in the blue sky, the still water, the occasional laugh of a child splashing in the ocean. If only it could last forever.

With his eyes still closed, he murmured. "Was that a sigh of contentment?"

Unwilling to disturb his languor, she said simply. "Yes."

He reached out and brushed his palm over the calf of her leg. "You're getting warm. You'll pick up more tan."

A flush heated her face. He hadn't opened his eyes. He didn't need to. He knew the colors and shades of her body without looking. He'd told her this morning how he loved her golden skin and how he meant to lie out in the sun with her in his garden and watch the paler places on her body turn as golden as the rest of her.

"You like it here in Key West, under the sun, don't you?"

He was quiet for a moment. Then he said, "I'll be busy rehearsing until the concert, but after that, we'll make up for lost time."

Toni looked at him helplessly, knowing that she had to tell him the truth. "Cay, I'll . . . be leaving Key West after your concert." She had plunged in, but the water was cold. So cold.

He lay unmoving, his eyes closed. "Establishing limits, Toni?" he finally said.

She averted her eyes from the sleek beauty of his body—the body she now knew better than she had ever known another man's. She knew the curve of his shoulders, the indentation at the base of his spine where he was incredibly sensitive, the feel of his muscular thighs rubbing against hers . . .

"There are always limits to any relationship."

"And you're saying that with you, I can damn well take what I get." The harsh words were a surprise.

"I wanted to be honest with you."

"Damn your honesty."

The mood of the day was broken. Cay lay tense with anger. The line of his jaw was taut. His arms were no longer relaxed at his sides. She moved, intending to go for a swim and work off her own tension.

"What are you doing?"

"Going for a swim."

He sat up. "Not without me, you're not."

She didn't want him out there in the water with her, but she knew it was useless to argue with him. "Suit yourself."

She didn't envision him using a romp in the ocean for a subtle game of sensual warfare, but she'd underestimated him. It all started innocently enough. He clasped a hand around her waist as they waded out to the deep water together and then swam beside her.

But suddenly she became aware of small encroachments—his foot touching hers; a hand gliding up her thigh and cupping her derriere; a palm at the small of her back, slithering up to the wet silky nape of her neck; and lastly, the brush of fingers against her breast—fingers that delved knowingly under the thick silk of her bikini bra for the nipple that was already hardening with desire.

Determined to stop him, she swam harder, flailing her arms and legs in an attempt to ward off his caresses.

He pulled her upright into his arms and kissed her while they sank below the surface of the water. A powerful kick of his legs sent them to the surface again.

"Cay," she gasped. "This is dangerous."

"Then you should enjoy it," he said silkily. "You like to live dangerously."

He was in the same strange mood when they returned to the house. In a curt tone, he asked Morry to order Chinese food for two and then asked rather pointedly what the older man intended to do that evening. Morry mumbled something about paperwork, gave Cay a glare and disappeared down the hall and into a room Toni supposed was his.

The food came. Cay gathered up the cardboard boxes, went into the kitchen and came back with a bottle of wine and the food on a tray.

"We're going upstairs."

Feeling hot from the sun and sticky from the salt and sand of the ocean, Toni stared at him helplessly. "Why?"

"Because we're going to have dinner in bed, the way lovers do."

"Cay—"

"You've only given me two and a half weeks," he said in a cool tone. "Can you blame me for wanting to make the most of the time we have?"

8

WHETHER IT WAS through Cay's design or by chance, Toni didn't know, but during the next two days the big cool bed in his room became the center of her life. She ate supper sprawled in comfort beside him, talking with him, touching him, loving him. During the day, Cay rehearsed for the concert he was going to give, driving himself relentlessly. Afternoons, Toni sat in the music room and listened to him play, enjoying every bittersweet minute of seeing and hearing him.

Each day she vowed she would stay away, but the compelling force of his music brought her to the open door and then into the room to stretch out on the couch he'd moved in for her. There was a forbidden fascination in watching him practice. The room had lost its barren splendor. He'd brought in four electric keyboards and arranged them together with the grand piano in a circle around him. Wearing nothing but cutoffs, he moved from one keyboard to another, a sheen of perspiration on his shoulders and face.

He practiced with utter self-absorption that it seemed he was communing with some force larger than himself to draw the music into his mind and out from his fingertips. His drive toward perfection continued into his lovemaking. His caresses were more subtle, more insidious, more mind-destroying. Each moment was exquisite torture, and she was powerless to stop him.

"I need you," he'd whisper to her at night. "I need to know you're there when I'm playing . . . and I need you now."

Caught in the spell of his vulnerable words, she whispered back, "I need you, too. So much . . ."

Through it all ran a current of restlessness. He drove himself down a path toward a musical perfection that was as elusive as smoke, and she was helpless to do anything but watch.

In the two days she'd been with him, she'd grown used to waking in the morning, feeling Cay's lean body beside her and his lips brushing hers. The rising sun would splash its light over his face while he made love to her, tenderly, thoroughly.

When she woke the third morning to find herself alone, she was filled with a sense of loss. Each minute with Cay was precious. She didn't want to miss a single one.

She was still harboring a vague sense that something was amiss a few minutes later when she entered Cay's bright sunlit kitchen, which was decorated with a shower of plants and dangling copper pots. She found Morry elbow-deep in flour dough, a cigar clamped between his teeth.

He greeted her gruffly, but not unkindly, and invited her to help herself to coffee. She wandered to the coffee maker, which was tucked back in the corner on the spotless counter, poured herself a cup and went to the window to look out into the garden. Even at this hour, its shadowy coolness beckoned.

Carefully casual, she asked, "Morry, where's Cay?" She'd struck a truce of sorts with the older man during the past few days that seemed to be holding.

"He's having photos taken for publicity stills at the old lighthouse."

Toni lowered her coffee mug very carefully to the table. Cay was out somewhere on the island posing for a photographer? He was a sitting duck. How could a talented, intelligent man be so stupid?

In the warm kitchen, she felt chilled. To Morry's back, which was bent slightly as he worked over his floured board, she said, "Why aren't you with him?"

"My instructions were to stay here with you." He sounded cool, annoyed.

"Your job is to protect Cay."

"My job is to follow his instructions."

"You shouldn't have let him go alone."

Morry turned around slowly, his flour-covered hands held out in front of him. "He's a big boy. He can take care of himself in broad daylight in a public place." Morry leaned back against the counter, his eyes watchful.

"We were in broad daylight in a public place last Friday night at that restaurant."

The look he gave her was the kind of look a male gives a female when he thinks she's out of line. "He put off having these pictures taken for two weeks."

Now she knew why Morry had that expression on his face. He believed she was the reason Cay hadn't wanted to take the time for a picture-taking session. "He couldn't put it off any longer. If he did, the committee wouldn't have any up-to-date glossies to promote the

sale of those high-priced charity tickets. He'll be all
right. Nothing's going to happen to Cay."

"You're darn right nothing's going to happen to him.
Where are your car keys?"

"Now listen, my friend, don't you do anything foolish. You're to stay here until he comes back."

"You're beginning to sound like Cay."

Morry didn't change his expression. "He doesn't want
anything to happen to you and neither do I."

"I'll be perfectly safe—" she gave Morry a knowing
look "—in broad daylight. Isn't that what you said?"

"If I have to hog-tie you—"

She was beginning to like Morry, especially at times
like these. He was trying so hard to look forbidding and
failing at it so completely with his flour-covered hands
and his worried eyes. "You'd better not try. You will be
a sweetheart and loan me your car, won't you?"

Morry sighed, half with exasperation, half with admiration. He was already wiping his hands on his
apron. She knew she had won. "Cay will have my
head."

"No, he won't; I'll save you."

"I can't think of one reason I should listen to you."

"The reason is . . . you care about Cay as much as I
do." Toni went to him and planted a kiss on his cheek.
"If anything happens, you can always say I told you so."

"Here, you wiseacre female," he said in a gruff tone
of affection, pulling the keys from his pocket. "Now get
out of here."

At ten o'clock in the morning, Key West looked
washed by the sun. Houses gleamed as if newly painted.
Palm trees rustled a friendly good-morning song. It

seemed impossible that anything bad could ever happen here.

The lighthouse, which was her destination, stood like a sentry above Old Town, yet was dwarfed when Toni compared it in her mind's eye to the modern condominiums and apartment houses of Miami. She squeezed Morry's Audi into a minuscule parking place two blocks away from it, got out and jogged the rest of the way.

When she got to the white picket fence surounding the lighthouse, she saw him. Cay stood in the lazily seductive stance that seemed to come natural to him, the sun playing over his dark head, his face smooth with boredom. The photographer was holding his light meter inches from Cay's classic nose.

The photographer grabbed his chin and pulled it around. "All right, Sinclair. Give me that dark, brooding sexy look."

Cay muttered something. Toni couldn't hear the word, but she could guess what it was.

"My, my, we are testy today, aren't we?"

"I don't know," Cay said dryly. "Are *we*?"

There was a turnstile between the fence and the house to keep non-paying customers out of the yard. Toni went over to it and wriggled through. There was a museum next to the lighthouse that was filled with memorabilia from World War II. Cay stood on the lawn as if he were facing a firing squad, his back to the rusted gray German submarine beached on the grass. His scowl didn't match his pirate garb. He was dressed in a white silk shirt that was unbuttoned to his navel, and he looked thoroughly unhappy.

Toni scanned the yard, and relief as sharp as a knife plunged through her. There was no one around but Cay and the photographer. She stepped a little closer and entered Cay's line of vision.

He shot away from the submarine toward her as if he'd been propelled from a torpedo tube. "What are you doing here? Are you alone? Where's Morry?"

Toni's eyes danced. "He's home saving his...dough."

Cay was not amused. "Dammit, what are you doing out without him?"

She lost her willingness to placate him. Her eyes changed to a steely silver that matched the fiery strength in his. "What are *you* doing out without him?"

His eyes flickered over her bare legs. She was dressed in her usual manner, shorts and a halter, and she hadn't given it a thought when she'd dashed out of the house. Now, watching Cay's mouth lift in sensual response as he perused her with lazy eyes, she wished she had thought.

"Did you come to be my keeper?"

"You need one."

"The job is open." The humor in his eyes seemed to come from some well deep inside him.

"You wouldn't want me. I'd keep you on a leash." She was furious that he would take such risks after the things Torgen had done. How could he be so stupid? "Look, hasn't it occurred to you that you're a sitting duck here?" She gestured around at the yard. The museum building stood on one side, the lighthouse on the other. "He could pop out at you from anywhere."

"Then why don't you stay and stand watch?" he asked, the glint in his eye at curious odds with the lazily relaxed posture of his body.

"I just might do that." He knew exactly how to challenge her, she realized, even as she fell into the trap.

The photographer ordered Cay into position again and gave his instructions. "All right, Sinclair. Don't smile. I don't want smiles from you. I want you to brood." Then Toni exacted her revenge.

She stood where Cay could see her and the photographer couldn't and showed him her idea of what the man wanted. She turned herself into a brooding beagle. Her mouth turned incredibly sad, as pulled down at the corners and as mournful as a clown's. Her eyes drooped, and her hands turned into floppy ears.

"All right now," said the photographer in his jolly schoolmaster's voice, "here we go."

Cay's eyes were drawn irresistibly to the glossy blackness of Toni's hair and to her face. The corners of his mouth went up.

The photographer lowered his camera and cast a disparaging look at Cay. Out of the corner of his eye, he saw Toni assume a normal expression. "Into little games today, are we?"

"Behave yourself," Cay said, the sun glinting in the green depths of his eyes as he shot Toni a warning look.

The photographer stepped forward and pulled Cay's shirt open another notch, exposing more of his chest. Toni's eyes wandered leisurely over him. *The star done in a star's trappings*, she thought. With his hair attractively tousled and his body exposed and turned to show off its lean strength to the best possible advantage, he was the stuff of women's dreams.

Her eyes lifted to his face . . . and she had never loved him more. Cay looked uncomfortable, and unless she was reading the expression in his eyes incorrectly, which she doubted, he was ready to reach out and strangle the photographer with his bare hands.

"If this wasn't a charity gig," Cay said pleasantly, "I'd take your camera and wrap it around your neck."

The photographer shot Cay a nervous look and was suddenly very concerned about a setting on his camera. Glancing at him uncertainly, he said, "Okay, now let's try it again. Remember, you gotta look serious to look sexy. That's it, give me a little of that restrained anger. Perfect. . . ."

Puffing out her cheeks, holding three fingers of each hand on top of her head for ears and crossing her eyes, Tony became a bear.

Cay exploded into laughter.

The photographer pulled his camera away from his face with a sigh. "Somehow, I'd thought I'd gotten away from this when I stopped working with kids. Look, Sinclair, could you possibly contain yourself for two seconds? If you can't—" the man swung around slowly and fastened a hard look on Toni "—I'm going to send your girlfriend up to the top of the lighthouse to watch for pirate ships."

Toni turned to the photographer. "Why don't you take pity on the guy and let him button up his shirt. Suggestion is much more sexy than exposure. Here, let me show you."

Standing in front of Cay, she said out of the corner of her mouth in her best gang moll imitation, "Want I should deck him?"

Cay's eyes danced with fire. "Want you should deck me."

As she tugged at the sides of his shirt to pull it closed, her fingers brushed his skin. Crisp hairs tickled her sensitive fingertips, and even while she fought both sensual memory and rising desire, he reached out and pulled her hips close to his.

"Would you like to know something, Mr. Sinclair?"

The corners of his extraordinary mouth tilted upward. "I'm always interested in improving my mind."

She slanted him a mock-sultry look from under her lashes. "You live up to every last word of your rotten reputation."

"How kind of you to say so." His touch became more possessive. He brought her hips tightly against his. The look in his eyes was total trouble. "You know, in the interest of my getting this session finished and our going home together, maybe you should go climb those tower stairs."

"No. I'm not leaving you."

His eyes darkened in a wonderful way that told her he was pleased. She knew what her words and the feel of her body against his was doing to him, and feeling a sudden sympathy for him, she nudged his arms, wordlessly asking for release.

He let go of her reluctantly and his eyes followed her as she went to stand behind the photographer again. This time, she kept her face and her hands still. She was as eager for him to be done as he was to finish.

He delivered the moods and the poses the photographer asked for as easily as a model. She could have stood there for hours watching the light play across his face and studying the interesting shadows in the hollows under his cheeks. She was almost surprised to discover that an hour had passed and the photographer had used up all the film he had and was packing up his gear.

"Lord. I feel like a calf let out of the barn on the first day of spring." Cay caught her hand and pulled her toward the open door of the tower. "Come on. I owe you something for those cute little faces. You are going to do penance, woman. I hereby sentence you to climbing the lighthouse stairs with me."

"No, no, have mercy!"

There was no mercy. She was pushed gently into the tower by Cay and propelled up the dark tunnel that held the most steeply winding, decidedly lethal, assuredly unending stairs she'd ever seen. She had to watch her step on the fan-shaped iron risers that seemed too narrow to hold her foot and at the same time fend off Cay's hand, which flicked at her rear rather more frequently than necessary "to help her keep her balance."

"Ninety-nine steps? Are you sure?" he said when they came out onto the walkway around the top of the tower, which offered them a spectacular view of the ocean.

"No, I'm not sure. I think I lost count somewhere after fifty-seven."

His hand sought, and found, the curve of her waist. "You really must improve your powers of concentration."

"Yes, I must. Oh, Cay, it's gorgeous." And it was. It was the same glorious mix of colors she'd seen everywhere in Key West—olive green palm trees, white, pink, gray and brown houses, and sapphire water—all seen from a bird's-eye view.

"Yes," he murmured, his back to the view, his eyes on her animated face, "it is indeed." His gaze was like a caress on her mouth. "Kiss me, Toni."

She complied, her mouth eager on his. The beauty of the day was now more complete.

Footsteps clanged on the stairs and two women emerged from the stairway. Toni broke away from Cay, feeling as if something precious had been snatched from her.

"Toni?" Putting his arm protectively around her, Cay turned her toward him. She buried her head against his chest.

"I'm not embarrassed. Just mad." She lifted her face to look at him. "I want each moment with you to be perfect."

There was a dark gleam in his eyes that didn't quite match the casual half smile on his mouth. "You don't have to worry about that."

She did, but she couldn't tell him that she'd decided to live each moment to the fullest and treasure her time with him as if each day were a precious diamond.

The spell was broken. "Let's go down," he said gently. "Uh-uh, nothing doing." He pulled her around behind him. "I go first. Then if you fall, you fall on me."

He was becoming too protective toward her, too possessive. She couldn't let him think that he had the right to—

Cay's boot heel clanged on the first of the metal stairs, and he pitched forward.

"Cay!" She grabbed for him frantically, her heart pounding. Her fingers connected with his shirt, but it was his own quick reaction that saved him. He fell to the side of the cement wall and wrapped his arms around the railing. "Cay," she cried, reaching for him.

"Don't move," he rasped harshly. "There's a wire strung across the top step."

She looked down the long, twisting staircase. If Cay had lost his footing, nothing would have stopped him from tumbling head over heels down the curving metal steps until he hit a wall . . . or landed at the bottom.

Dazed, she turned her eyes back to him. For an endless moment, he searched her face—her transparent face, which hid nothing from him. "Cay, give me your hand."

"I'll be all right." With one hand on the railing, Cay moved back toward her, pulled a knife from his pocket and clipped the nearly invisible wire. The ends were wrapped around a supporting post on either side of the staircase and neatly twisted. Stuck in one of the twisted ends was a feather.

"Torgen," she whispered.

"A guitar string. His idea of a joke. Damn fool. It could have been one of those women instead of me."

"But they just came out of the stairway a minute ago."

"He must have been following right on their heels. That's why we didn't hear him." Angrily Cay tossed the wire into the hollow center of the circular stairway where it click-clacked to the bottom. "The swine was quick. Come on. Let's get out of here."

All the way back to Cay's and through the lunch that Morry served, the vision of Cay tumbling down those stairs haunted Toni. Her knees seemed to have a tendency to tremble at odd moments.

After lunch, Cay put a gentle hand on her wrist and lifted her from her chair at the table. "I'm going to practice. Come with me."

Unable to think of doing anything else with his hand on hers, she obeyed. Climbing the stairs ahead of him, and then going into the music room, she settled on the couch. "Try not to think about it," he said softly. She nodded, ordering her mouth and her eyes to hide the disturbing thoughts, playing riot inside her head. She didn't want Cay to be worrying about her when he needed to make every moment of his practice time count. But despite her efforts, she could feel his dark eyes seeking her face, watching her over the top of the piano.

"You're not fooling me, you know," he said wnen, much later, they had finished eating their evening meal and Cay had pulled her down onto the couch with him. "You're still thinking about what happened this morning."

"Where will it end? What will he do next?"

He pressed her head against his chest and stroked her hair. "I don't know. I wish I did." She absorbed his soothing touch like a sponge, taking strength from him. He lifted her face to his and carefully, as if he were kissing a child, covered her mouth with his. Instantly the comfort vanished, replaced by something more basic, demanding and potent. "Why don't we go upstairs—" his voice was husky "—and I'll see if I can think of something for us to do that will take your mind off him."

FOR THE NEXT TWO DAYS, Toni's anxiety over Cay overrode the nagging voice that reminded her she had work to do. On Friday, she knew she couldn't wait any longer to check out her sound equipment in preparation for the concert the next night.

When she told Cay she was returning to her house, he said, "I'll go with you."

"No. You have your work to do. I have mine."

"You can't walk around the streets alone. I'll send the two men with you who've been watching this house."

Her eyes clear, she looked at him. "Please don't. I couldn't work with someone watching me every minute like a sentry."

He turned away as if there were something in his face he didn't want her to see. "Then get Liz to stay with you." His eyes flashed back to her face. "Otherwise, you're stuck with me."

"I can't take you away from your practicing. I'll call Liz."

"Go ahead." He gestured toward the telephone. "Call her now."

Toni talked to Liz, and Liz said she was free that afternoon. Toni thanked her, hung up and turned back to Cay.

"I'll come over and meet you at the house around five, if that's agreeable?" He sounded cool, as if her answer didn't interest him.

"Yes, of course." His indifference hurt her more than she believed possible.

Cay watched her go, savoring the sight of her slender body clad in shorts and a halter top as she gracefully went out the door. It had taken all the control he had to let her walk away. But he did it because he had to. Before, he'd been acting out of instinct with Toni, but now he had to think . . . and think hard.

It didn't take much thinking. When he'd made his decision, he placed one call to a florist and then dialed Liz. He was through with holding back and playing the game conventionally.

TO TONI, the house she'd shared with Liz looked strangely unreal. There was a coat of dust over everything, even the china cats, and the nude above the mantle . . . Toni stepped closer to inspect her face. The Mona Lisa smile no longer seemed like a leer. That smile contained knowledge—the knowledge of a woman who had been loved and loved very well. Toni's body pulsed with reaction. This was the first time in days that she had been in a house without Cay within calling distance, and her first thought brought him to mind with stinging clarity. She missed him.

Liz came out of the kitchen and walked around to look into Toni's face. "You look strange."

"Thank you."

"Is something wrong?"

Toni cast another quick glance at the nude and then turned away. "I think so. Got any iced tea?"

"No, but I'll make some."

A minute later, when Toni sat down at the kitchen table, Liz handed her a tall, cool glass and settled in the chair opposite her. "Are you going to tell me anything?"

"About what?"

"About Cay Sinclair." Liz frowned in impatience. "Are you falling in love with him?"

"No."

"No?" Liz looked shocked.

"Falling in love with someone means you can fall out again."

Comprehension flashed over Liz's face, and she gave Toni a sunny smile. "You've got it that bad for him, huh?"

Toni looked down at the icy drink she was twisting on the table. "Yes, I've got it that bad."

"Well, what are you going to do about it?"

"Nothing."

"Don't sit there and tell me you're going to do nothing."

Toni gave her a dry look. "What do you want me to do? Stand up?"

"Has he said anything?"

"No." Liz looked disturbed, more disturbed than she should have. "Do you . . . have any special reason for asking?"

Liz flushed. "Well, to tell you the truth, I was going to hand in my notice." At Toni's expression, Liz said, "Don't get me wrong. I'm going to finish out these last two concerts with you. But after that—" She stopped as if to gather herself together. "I love Tommy. He's the first man I've ever known who really cares about me.

One night, while we were out together, he told me to stop using those big words I use. He said I didn't have to do that to impress him. When he said that to me, I knew I loved him. Haven't you noticed I don't mangle my words anymore?"

Toni hadn't. There'd been too many other things to worry about—Cay's safety uppermost. "I'm so glad you're happy."

"I'm going to be even happier in a few weeks." She colored attractively. "We're going to get married and settle here in the Keys. He's got a job, and I can find something to do. I know I can."

"So that's the reason you were throwing me at Cay Sinclair's head."

Liz straightened in her chair. "Nobody throws you anywhere. You go where you want to go."

Toni leaned forward and covered Liz's hand with hers. "You're absolutely right. I'm the one who needs my head examined. Honey, I'll miss you, but you're my friend, and I wish you the best of everything."

"You'll stay for the wedding, won't you? I want you to be my maid of honor."

"When is it?"

"A month from today." Liz studied her anxiously.

Without thinking, she said quickly. "I'll be there."

LATER THAT DAY, Liz and Toni were in their van. Liz had insisted on coming along to act as watchdog. In front of Toni were a dozen electrical connections she had sprayed with an aerosol cleaner to nullify the effects of the Key West heat and moisture. She wiped her hand across her brow and it came away wet. "I'm thirsty. Liz, would you mind—"

In the front seat of the van, Liz wriggled in relief, glad of an excuse to escape the heat inside the vehicle. "More iced tea, coming up."

Toni went on working until she heard the van's front door close. "Thank goodness you're back," she said without looking up, "I was getting so thirsty—"

The silence sent the first prickle of fear down her back. The click of the lock of first one front door and then the other filled her with stark terror.

She lifted her head. Torgen sat in the driver's seat, his body turned toward her, his face wreathed in a beatific smile. In his khaki pants and army shirt, he looked like a terrorist.

"Hello, Miss Pereola. How are you?"

"I was a whole lot better a moment ago." She didn't know where she'd found the courage to be flippant. Her knees were shaking and her heart was going like a trip-hammer. There were so many things inside the van this demented man could use as weapons—wrenches, screwdrivers, the soldering gun with its heated tip . . .

"You've gone quite pale, my dear." He chuckled as if he were vastly pleased, and she realized that he enjoyed frightening her. "You don't have to be afraid of me, you know. All you have to do is agree to act as my messenger."

"Do I look like Western Union?" she said through gritted teeth.

His smile vanished as if it had been wiped off his face. "You're such a clever little girl. Maybe you're too clever for your own good." He half rose off his seat and lifted a hand toward her, and she saw that he wore black leather gloves. "Now listen to me. You tell Mr. Cay Sinclair that we want more money, and we won't wait any longer. We want it now."

"We?"

"We. Marisa. Me. We're tired of living on the pittance he allotted us. We want more." He lifted his gloved hand and stabbed a finger at her. "Tell him today."

Toni raised her head and met the man's glittery eyes. "You were close enough to him at the lighthouse to deliver your own message."

Torgen shook his head slowly. "No. It will have more impact coming from you." He gave her another of his beatific smiles.

Toni faced him, fury in her eye. "You nearly killed Cay." She wanted to slap the look of bland innocence off his face.

With the air of a wronged man, he said, "I haven't the faintest idea what you're talking about."

"I'm not helping you with your rotten extortion schemes!"

"You'd better help me, Miss Pereola. Your life depends on it. Think about that before you make any brave, stupid decisions."

With the fluid movement of an eel, he opened the door and slid out. In the next moment, he was gone.

Shaking with nerves and fury, Toni sank forward on her knees on the carpeted floor. By now, pursuit was futile. There were a hundred other things she could have done. She could have hit him over the head with a screwdriver. She could have kept him talking until Liz saw him and called the police. She could have . . .

"What are you doing? What's wrong?" Liz asked as she popped into the driver's seat, holding the iced tea, her face wreathed in concern.

Toni took a deep breath and told her what had happened.

"Oh, Toni—" Liz nearly spilled the iced tea over the back of the driver's seat "—I knew I shouldn't have left you alone. But I was only gone for a minute. We've got to tell Cay about this."

"No. Let me handle it."

Liz looked worried. "You are going to tell him, aren't you?"

"I'm not sure that I am. What good would it do? Cay obviously knows what the man wants, and he hasn't given in to him. Why would one more threat make a difference?"

"Toni, you've got to tell him."

"No, not just yet. And you're not going to, either." She braced her hands on her bare thighs and stared at Liz. "He must have been watching us. He knew the moment you left me."

Liz shivered. "Please stop talking about him. You're giving me the jitters. You make me feel like he's all around us—everywhere."

Toni remembered feeling the same way. Even while she'd been gazing down at Key West and feeling euphoric, he'd been creeping up the lighthouse stairs. "It's fear that makes you think that. Fear is his stock-in-trade." Against her thighs, Toni's hands curled into fists. "I'd like to turn the tables on him."

"Scare him, you mean? How could you do that?"

"I don't know. I really don't know."

For the rest of the day, with Liz glued to her side except for one long, rather odd interval, Toni thought about the problem of trapping Torgen with his own fear. There had to be a way.

She was still thinking about it when Cay picked her up at the house and took her out to dinner. They chose a restaurant that had a private room. All through the meal, Cay's eyes kept flickering back to Toni as if there was something about her that bothered him.

Evidently there was. They finished eating and he guided her back to the car. Feeling more than exhausted by her encounter with Torgen, she settled into the car and tipped her head back on the seat.

As they drove through the Key West night, oncoming traffic spotlighted Cay's face intermittently, giving her glimpses of his lean profile, his classic nose. Suddenly she knew why he was acting so formally polite.

"You know what happened and you're angry with me because I didn't tell you."

His hands tightened on the wheel. "Luckily Liz and I made a pact that first night. She was wise enough not to break it." They reached Toni's house and he pulled into the driveway and shut off the motor, but he didn't turn and look at her. "I thought you and I had a pact of sorts, too. Why didn't you tell me?"

She twisted in her seat, her face anguished. "What good would it have done? You knew Torgen wanted money." She lifted a hand and pushed back a lock of hair. "I didn't want to add any more pressure to your life right now, that's all."

"And you were afraid if you did tell me, I'd be convinced you were helping him."

"That possibility did occur to me."

Cay was silent for a moment, his face dark. "I deserved that dose of my own medicine, I suppose. But that doesn't mean I like it." He captured her face between his palms. "If I had any remaining doubts, which I'm not sure I did, you erased every one of them. The look on this sweet face the day I nearly went head over heels down those lighthouse stairs told me everything I needed to know." Her relief was so palpable that he could see it, feel it. He gave her a fierce, brief kiss. "I've prepared something in the way of an apology. Sweetheart, come inside with me."

In a daze, her fingers touching his cheek, she said, "We're at the wrong house."

"Oh no, we're not," he breathed with husky intensity, as his eyes drifted over her face and his mouth took on a familiar sensuous droop. "This house has something I need tonight." Tucking a strand of hair behind her ear, he murmured, "We're going to go inside and you're going to go up and change into something cool and comfortable." He pushed her out of the car and into the house with the fluid ease and male determination she was beginning to recognize as belonging to a man determined to sweep the world away and spend a time of intimacy with his woman.

Even more familiar to her were her own responses to Cay's mood. Her pulse quickened, her skin warmed, and another heat began deep within her.

After Cay repeated his instructions about her mode of dress, gave her a dictatorial pat on her rear to send her on her way and disappeared into the kitchen, she climbed the stairs, her heart pounding in anticipation, her mind racing ahead in a plan.

9

A FEW MINUTES LATER, Cay appeared at the door of Toni's bedroom, bearing a wine bottle in ice and two glasses on a tray. "Thought you might be thirsty after that meal of snapper—"

Fire caught in his eyes as he looked at her. She sat on her heels in the bed, her knees tucked under her, her hair combed, her lips touched with color. Her face revealed a dozen different expressions—apprehension, hopefulness...and a tentative smile. She looked like a child...except that she wore a turquoise teddy made of lustrous silk that revealed the uplift of her breasts in luscious detail.

"You got comfortable in a hurry."

"Yes, didn't I?" she said honestly, her gray eyes meeting his green ones and silently pleading for his casual acceptance. "Are we having Lambrusco?"

A slight flush lay under her cheeks. He held the tray and looked at her, his heart bursting. There was no reason for her to be nervous, she'd made love with him many times before. Yet in that way he had of understanding her, he knew that this was another hurdle for her. She'd never done this, never played the part of a wanton and dressed to please him. What courage it must have taken for her to do so now, he thought.

He wanted to say so many things to her, but for the first time in his life, he was afraid. And he had a surprise of his own waiting for her. If she didn't like what he'd done... "Yes, that's what we're having," he told her. "Among—" his eyes played over her bare legs "—other things."

Her color deepened, but he could see her making a gallant effort to hide her nervousness. "Did you bring napkins? I don't want to spill any wine on . . . this."

"Spill away." He hesitated and then said in a carefully bland tone, "I'll buy you another."

How closely his eyes watched her, Toni thought. How difficult it was not to react to the first mention he'd made of their staying together. How to answer him in a way that wouldn't reveal how much she loved him? "This material is stronger than it looks." She, too, could play the watching game, but his face was as smooth as a water-washed stone. "I won't need another for a while."

He didn't move. He stood at the side of the bed, holding the tray, his eyes as unrevealing as she'd ever seen them. "Perhaps you will. The way you look wearing it, it might suffer more than the normal wear and tear. Particularly," he said, his voice becoming husky, "since I'm about to rip it off you."

"Cay, you aren't." She suddenly felt breathless.

His eyes told her he would like to. "You prefer to take your bath with it on?"

"Who said I was taking a bath?"

"I did."

As graceful as a cat, he bent over the table next to the bed and deposited the tray. "It seems we both had surprises planned tonight." Without blinking an eye, in one smooth move of continuous upward motion he scooped her off the bed.

"Cay—" She laughed and kicked her legs, but the hard strength of his arms was unyielding. She tingled with awareness of him, conscious of her unbound breasts under the silky material that were already stinging in anticipation and the press of his fingers against her bare thighs.

Cay nudged open the door of the opulent bathroom and stood with her in his arms, turning slightly to give her a better view of the surprise he'd planned for her.

The perfume of a million flowers drifted to her nose. The bright heads of hibiscuses spilled over every available surface. They covered the counter, dripped from the side of the bathtub, lay bunched in colorful profusion in the corners. Several had fallen into the bathwater and floated serenely there, becoming delicious boats made of petals and long spidery stamens that could be destroyed by a touch.

"How did you manage this?" Toni asked faintly.

"Liz arranged for the florist to have a key while we were out eating. Do you like it?"

She said nothing. His grip on her loosened and he let her slide to her feet. Turning to face the bower of beauty he'd created, he said huskily, "You told me you loved flowers, but you'd never had any of your own. I wanted you to have these." He paused. "Toni, say something."

She turned to him, her eyes closed, her mind writhing in helpless knowledge that he was taking too much from her, too much, and she was powerless to stop him.

"Toni, what is it? For God's sake, what is it?"

She couldn't let him see how much this gesture of his had deepened her love for him yet widened the gulf between them. He was capable of giving her anything she wanted except what she wanted most—his heart. "It's too . . . beautiful."

"Yes," he breathed, "like you." He brushed aside the straps of her teddy, and with his eyes becoming dark and possessive, he pulled the slippery bit of nothing down and off her body.

The water in the tub was silk, and Cay's skin was silk, and they blended to give her a sensual ecstasy she'd never known before. He made love to her with the slow concentration of a hedonist king, his hands and mouth gliding over her wet skin and discovering new treasures with each foray.

A red hibiscus bobbed against his chest, a scarlet bird on bronzed flesh. He plucked it out of the water and threaded it into her hair above her ear. As his wet hand passed over her, a drop of water fell on the curve of her breast and trickled on a slow, devastating path downward. He saw it . . . and followed it with his tongue.

When he raised his head, he gazed into her love-filled eyes and murmured, "When you look at me that way, you destroy me. Ah, Toni—" He pulled her close and with infinite care, fit his body into hers.

The water slid like satin over her skin. His tongue claimed the mouth that was already his, and his body echoed his primitive possession. She moved and he moved, and they were one with the water and the flowers . . . and the universe.

IN THE MORNING, Toni lay beside Cay, forcing herself to tolerate the lazily marauding finger tracing teasing circles around her abdomen.

"You will bring that intriguing garment you had on last night back to the house with you, won't you?" Cay paused. "Along with the rest of your things."

"Cay, I . . . can't think when you're doing that."

"Who asked you to think?" His touch drugged her, made her mind want to drift behind her eyelids, which were already drooping.

"You can't go on living with just my shirt and toothbrush and the few things you brought. Not that I wouldn't enjoy seeing you try, you understand—" Cay wasn't thinking, he was acting on instinct—sheer jungle instinct. He was pressing his advantage, which was something he'd learned long ago how to do . . . and had somehow restrained himself from doing with her. Now, ruthlessly, he looked down at Toni's pagan loveliness and knew that the time for being scrupulously careful was past. "Want me to help you pack?" His hand made a swoop and turned upward to explore the lovely burgundy crest that flowered at his touch.

She caught his head between her hands and kept him from taking the kiss he was going to steal from her lips. "You're doing this on purpose."

"Smart lady," he murmured against her mouth. "I certainly am." He took her mouth leisurely, in the way a male arrogantly reclaims what he knows is his. "Are you going to pack?" His hand slid down the length of her body, discovering each sleek curve and dip of her ribs, her waist, her thighs.

"No, no—"

He lowered his head and his tongue traced an agonizingly slow path around the crown of her breast. "Say yes, Toni," he breathed, feeling that what had started out to be her punishment was fast becoming his.

"No...no..." He covered her nipple with his mouth, and she breathed in sharply. "Yes—"

A few hours later, he leaned against he door of his bedroom and watched as she put the things she had brought into the bureau drawer he had cleared for her. He wasn't enjoying his victory. She was too quiet, and he didn't like the look on her face. "Toni. What's wrong?"

She raised her silver eyes to him. "I was thinking about how I was persuaded to do something I didn't want to do with such...finesse." She closed the drawer and looked up at him. "You're quite accomplished at getting what you want."

He didn't know what she was saying. Was she worrying about her independence or was she trying to tell him something else, something important that he should understand but didn't? "I hope you weren't offended."

To Toni, Cay looked tense, apprehensive. How sensitive he was . . . to everything but her love for him. "I was wondering if I could find something else to argue with you about."

He came away from the door, his tension fading, a roguish smile tugging at his lips. "With your flair for obstinacy, I'm sure you can."

Toni raised an eyebrow. "And you'll deal with my resistance in the same way?"

He took her into his arms. "If that's what you want. Or—" his hand traveled slowly down her back "—we might explore a few variations on the theme."

THE NIGHT of the third concert, Cay accompanied Toni and Liz to the concert site on Duval Street. There was a brooding quietness about him matched by the darkness in his eyes. Toni's worry about Cay's mood made it difficult for her to concentrate on the setup for the concert, but with Liz's help, she managed. The performing group was a Dixieland jazz band, and the men were black, older and angels to work with. They accepted her advice and teased her about her occupation, telling her she was doing a man's job, then dedicated their first number, "Sweet Georgia Brown," to her. The evening was a welcome break from the cloud of tension she'd been under, thinking about Cay.

During the next few days, she saw little of him. He'd moved his keyboards out of the music room and into the renovated barn on Duval Street in Old Town where the concert was to be held, and he'd go there early and stay until the wee hours of the morning. When he'd climb into the big bed, he wouldn't reach for her.

His indifference to her was natural enough, Toni told herself with a fierce earnestness. Cay hadn't performed for a live audience in five years, and he needed every minute to prepare himself. But when she lay in bed alone and remembered that night she'd lain with him in the silky water surrounded by hibiscus blossoms, her body ached with need.

Her need was more than a physical one. She needed him mentally and emotionally. She needed his love. Could she go on living with him this way, never knowing what the outcome of their relationship would be?

She had no choice. She'd never had a choice, not from the first moment she'd seen him. . . .

The day before Cay's concert, Toni began to move her own equipment to the barn. While Liz hauled things in, Toni raced around like a madwoman, finding a power source, making connections and praying that the fuses wouldn't blow when she turned everything on. The air-conditioning hadn't been turned on in the cavernous building, and by the time she had the huge bins placed in the back where she wanted them and the stage monitors positioned to Cay's specifications, she was dripping with perspiration.

Then they had to do a sound check. Cay had given her a copy of his concert program and indicated the places he thought she would have to listen for special problems.

It was only when they'd run through most of the songs that Cay dropped his bombshell.

"I'll only need the mike for the last number."

"What are you talking about?" Toni asked, puzzled.

"I'm doing the last number with acoustical guitar sitting on a stool out front. I'll see about getting someone to shift the mike for me."

She went cold. "Suppose Torgen decides to take a potshot at you?"

Unperturbed, he said coolly, "Suppose he does?"

She felt a chill go down her spine. "You've already thought about it."

"Yes, I've thought about it. It's exactly the kind of thing he might do. The perfect irony, destroying me in front of the first audience I've had in five years."

"You can't let that happen," she said, her eyes searching his face avidly for a sign that he didn't mean it.

The coolness she had seen often in the last few days and had come to recognize and dread came into his eyes. "What can I do to stop him?"

She couldn't bear the thought of how vulnerable he would be. She'd comforted herself during the past week, thinking he wouldn't be a target, surrounded as he was by his keyboards. But if he sat alone at center stage . . . "Tell the police. Hire security guards and surround the theater with them. You can't risk your life this way."

"You should know by now that no security guard is going to stop Torgen. And I'm damn well not going to perform behind an armed cordon."

"Then cancel the concert."

He shook his head. "No."

Thoroughly exasperated, Toni said, "You're carrying this 'the show must go on' tradition too far. One concert is not worth the risk," she pleaded, feeling sick with dread.

He was unmoved. "I've made a commitment, and I'm not going to back out just because a man I used to call *friend* has threatened me."

Toni worried for the rest of the day. *Think, mind, think.* But it wasn't until the middle of the afternoon, when one of the fuses blew and threw the theater into complete darkness, that she had a brainstorm.

She sent Liz out for extra tapes. Cay had asked her to record the concert through the tape deck installed in the mixing board, but along with the lights, she needed a spare audio cassette for her plan....

By eight they were ready for a straight run-through. They finished at ten with nothing but a few minor hitches, and Cay declared that he was satisfied. "We'll do a repeat for the lighting crew in the morning."

It was Toni's turn to drop a bomb. "Let Liz do the lighting."

From the stage, Cay's voice rose hoarsely and carried with icy precision to every corner of the two-hundred-fifty-seat theater. "I hired an outfit from Miami to do the lighting. They'll be here tomorrow."

Toni lifted her chin. "I want Liz to do it."

He shook his head. "I've already made arrangements."

"Cancel them. Get some local electricians to change the configurations and the wiring so Liz and I can control everything from down here."

"You'll be too damn busy to—"

Interrupting in a cool, rapier tone, she said, "Or get yourself another sound engineer."

Cay leaped off the stage and strode down the aisle to the middle of the theater where she'd set up her board. "You're not walking out on me now."

She met his eyes steadily, knowing he thought she was doing it because of their unresolved personal life, but she couldn't go into a long, involved explanation in front of Liz and the techs—particularly since she needed secrecy if she wanted her plan to be effective. For the moment, Cay would have to think whatever he liked. "Then let me do this the way I think it should be done."

Toni looked exactly as she had the first night he'd seen her. She was wearing her working clothes—black shorts and black halter top and the black ballet slippers that she flew around in. She was fierce, determined, single-minded, obstinate, delectable. God, it had been too long. He remembered the scent of her skin, the feel of her hair brushing his throat . . . and the way he'd been staying away from her. He'd been protecting himself, steeling himself for exactly this. His gut instinct had been right. He'd known she'd find a reason to leave him, that she wouldn't just walk away. What he hadn't suspected was that she'd create a conflict in their professional relationship to destroy their personal bond.

Now she had her reason, and it was perfect. She had the ideal excuse to walk out on him—unless he took it away from her. He gritted his teeth. "All right, Toni. I'll get the electricians in here tomorrow."

He could see that she was surprised, but it gave him very little satisfaction.

THE NEXT MORNING, it took an hour to restring the lighting the way Toni wanted it and another hour to add controls for the houselights to the board. When the techs finished, Toni heaved a sigh of relief. Cay appeared shortly after that, and they finished the final run-through by one.

Coming out of the theater, Toni found the sun too bright for her and closed her eyes against its brilliance.

Her arm was seized. Cay stood on the sidewalk beside her, looking slightly menacing. "I've already locked your van. Leave it. You're riding home with me."

His quiet fury made her make her own mental adjustments, preparing for the war that seemed imminent. He was silent all the way home, silent as he helped her from the car, silent as he pushed her into the house and trundled her up the stairs. With Cay holding her elbow in an ironlike grip, she had little choice but to do as he wanted.

Once they were in the bedroom, he pushed her gently down on the bed. "Now that we're in the place where we communicate best, would you like to explain why you're taking over the lighting?"

Her backbone straightened as if pulled by a string and she stood up. "This is the last place I'd talk to you about my work."

"Well, you're going to start talking," he said in a mock-pleasant tone that sent cold fear shivering down her spine.

Her eyes were pure molten silver. In her flat slippers, she seemed ridiculously short. "You say there's nothing I can do to protect you from Torgen. Well, you're wrong. You're carrying some kind of ridiculous guilt complex where he's concerned because you wanted to quit, and he didn't, and after you stopped playing, his career crashed. You may like to play Don Quixote, but I'm not going to stand around and watch you do it. I'm going to stop him, but to do that, I need control of the lighting."

She could see that her explanation threw him. What had he expected her to say? Didn't he know how much she cared for him?

"What are you going to do?" he said slowly.

"I'm not sure yet. I don't have it all worked out."

"Why?"

"Why? Spare me from musicians who think they're the only ones who have anything to do to get ready for a concert. Because, in case it's slipped your notice, I've been busy."

"I don't mean that. I mean why are you plotting to save my hide?"

"I asked myself that several times this morning," she said with a tinge of sharpness. "I didn't come up with an answer."

"Didn't you?" he replied softly, intently. "Toni, listen. You don't have to prove yourself to me. I believe in you."

She should have been rejoicing. That was what she'd been waiting, praying to hear him say. But it no longer seemed important. There was something much more vital at stake—Cay's life. With heated fervor, she said, "That's wonderful. I'm glad. Very glad. But it doesn't change anything. I'm not going to stand by and let you turn yourself into a sitting duck for Torgen's shooting gallery."

"Why should you care if Torgen tries to take a potshot at me?"

She glared at him. "Don't tell me you don't know the answer to that."

"It isn't because you . . . care for me."

"No, of course not," she said in a bitter tone that hid her pain. "Why should I care about you? You're an egotistical, arrogant—"

"Temporary," he put in, his eyes as cool as an Arctic wind. "I'm temporary."

She felt as if the breath had been knocked from her body.

"What's the matter? Didn't you know I understand how you feel about me? I know you think I am as incapable of sustaining a long-term relationship as your last lover."

"That's not true."

"Don't lie to me, Toni. Not after—" he gave her a slight, self-mocking smile "—I've come to depend on your unflinching honesty." He raised his hand and teasingly stroked her cheek with his lean finger. The tender potency in his touch nearly broke her heart. "After tonight, your work is finished in Key West. You no longer have to stay here. Are you waiting until after the concert to tell me you're leaving?"

"No. No."

"Will you stay?" When she didn't answer, he said, "The truth, sweetheart."

Would she stay? When he asked her just like that, with a cool, appraising look on his face and not a hint of his own feeling betrayed in his eyes or his face or his mouth, dammit, no, she wouldn't stay. He had a nerve bringing her here on the day of his concert and forcing her to answer the question she'd been asking herself for the last two weeks. No, that wasn't right. She hadn't been asking herself if she could stay. She'd been asking herself how she could ever bear to go.

It took all the courage she had to raise her chin and look him in the eye. "I'll stay for as long as you want me."

Afterward, he never knew what drove him on to make her surrender complete. It was as if some dark force over which he had no control impelled the words from his mouth. "Without knowing how long that will be?"

She didn't flinch. "Yes."

He pulled her into his arms, his heart full with admiration and love for her. God, yes, love. It had always been love. How he needed her! And never more than at this moment. His head dropped to graze the curved flesh above her halter top.

Toni clung to the thought that Cay would be going on stage in a few short hours. "Darling, be reasonable. It's only seven hours until your concert—"

He said in an urbanely amused tone, "Several hours should be long enough to accomplish what I have in mind."

"But there's something we have to do together." Her hands lifted to his chest and slid up slowly, half in protest, half in sensuous discovery.

"My sentiments exactly."

"Cay, we need to—" his mouth traced around her earlobe, and she had to struggle to recapture her thought "—go back to the theater. I have to record your voice and mix the recording to play into the four different speakers." He loosened the halter tie at her nape with a flick of his fingers and smoothed the strings down over her shoulders. In the next instant her halter was gone, and Cay was lovingly exploring the rise of her breast with his mouth. She fought to hold on to the one coherent thought she had. "Cay, please. I can't think when you do that.... If Torgen does come, you'll be entrusting me with your life."

Bearing her down on the bed with him, he murmured, "I already have."

"Cay, please, you must listen to me—"

"And I will. Later." He stopped her last futile attempt to talk by covering her mouth with his.

10

THAT NIGHT, as the hour of Cay's concert approached, excitement lit Key West like a filament stretching from one end of the island to the other. Toni remembered some graffiti she'd seen on the wall of an abandoned building on Duval Street.

"Key West has no snow, no first run movies, no beaches, no surfing." Below it had been added in big letters "Eat your heart out, baby. Cay Sinclair is here!"

Even though the tickets were reserved seating, the crowd began to line up outside the theater two hours before concert time.

Inside, Toni watched Liz run a final check on the lighting. She flicked a switch and the stage lights went off; another, and the houselights were extinguished; another, and the spotlights went out. A blank tape was loaded in the recorder, but another, the one Toni had recorded with Cay an hour before, lay within easy reach.

As it usually did when Toni was trying to make a last-minute check on all the connections, the clock raced— and so did her heart. Would Torgen show up? A voice inside her head told her it was possible. Cay was right; it was the kind of thing he would do. Torgen said he wanted money, but his actions seemed to be motivated by a streak of vindictive jealousy.

Why hadn't the drummer gone on and made a career for himself after his stint with Cay? Why had he given up his career in music and made a career of harassing Cay? She should have asked Ferguson more questions.

She sat down on the stool and stared at the empty stage. The theater buzzed with anticipation. Half an hour ago, she'd been backstage with Cay in his dressing room, watching him submit with bored irritation to the ministrations of the makeup man. An unmade-up face caught in the bright spotlights Cay used had a tendency to look green. She'd sat for a few minutes and then decided it would be better if she left. As she'd gotten to her feet, he'd caught her wrist.

"Aren't you forgetting something?" he'd asked. At her puzzled look, he said, "I need a kiss for good luck."

"You'll do fine."

He smiled roguishly. "There's nothing like a little insurance, just to make certain."

"I'll ruin your makeup."

"And I'll enjoy every minute of it."

At exactly eight o'clock, his makeup repaired, Cay strolled onto the stage. Toni was seated in the middle of the audience, surrounded by the U-shaped prison of her equipment, so perhaps it was only natural that his eyes went directly to her. She couldn't be more than a dark form to him. She'd stood on the stage an hour ago and discovered just how blinding the spotlights were.

Cay bowed to acknowledge the wild applause just once. When he settled himself inside his nest of keyboards, the crowd quieted immediately. He began to sing, and there wasn't another sound in the house.

Toni had spent many hours listening to him practice, but those hours in the music room hadn't prepared her for the impact of Cay Sinclair in concert. He seemed filled with a vital force, which poured out of him through his fingers and his voice. With his lean face drawn in lines of intense concentration, he sang of the joy to be found in the arms of a lover. While one part of Toni remained as methodical and businesslike as any sound engineer, another part whispered that Cay was singing this song differently than he had a few days ago. Behind the professional delivery was a new depth of meaning, a greater range of emotion. He wasn't just singing the words. He was living them. And because he was living them, so did she . . . and everyone else in the theater. By the second half of the song, the hushed quiet told Toni that they knew, just as she did, that the kind of performance they were hearing tonight was as rare as a perfect diamond.

He wasn't looking at her now. His head was turned and his eyes were half closed. Never had a man looked more powerful, sounded more talented...or been more magnetic.

Cay moved from strength to strength. He sang about the bleakness of a Monday morning when a lover is no longer there. Toni closed her mind to the whispery seduction of that velvet-sad sound. The E-mu needed toning down through the middle range and she had to keep a close eye on the monitor for the drum machine.

He went on singing, using his voice and his fingers to create a siren call to the soul, spinning a web that ensnared every one of the two hundred fifty people in the renovated barn. Toni listened, and yet another part of her mind worried. Would that siren call bring Torgen into the theater? And if it did, would the trap she'd set for him work?

The time for intermission came, and amid the shouts and clapping, Cay left the stage. Twenty minutes went by—twenty minutes that felt like two hours. Toni stayed where she was on her stool, her eyes searching the lighted theater. She didn't know exactly what she should be looking for. If Torgen was in the crowd, but was wearing a different costume tonight, her eyes might slide right over him.

Liz, who was sitting next to Toni, whispered, "Do you see him?"

"No. You're sure you know what to do?"

"I hope so," Liz sighed.

"There's the signal. Blink the houselights."

Toni's nerves tightened as Cay strolled on the stage for the second part of the show. The next two numbers would be instrumentals. They had been placed after the intermission to give his voice the maximum amount of time to rest. Both were new pieces of music that he had written for the show.

What followed was a virtuoso display of technique and sensitive musicianship that surpassed the concert

Toni had heard five years before. Cay's music had taken on the soaring strength of the ocean, the mysteries of secret caves, the towering strength of mountains. He drew cries and whispers, and chords of eerie beauty from his electronic keyboards, putting to rest forever the idea that electrical instruments could not be artistic. In Cay's hands, everything became a medium through which his artistry traveled.

At the end of his last instrumental number, the crowd burst into wild applause. Toni let out a long-held breath. There had been no sign of Torgen. Was it possible the man had sense enough not to disrupt a concert?

"My last song is a new one," Cay said from the stage. "I call it 'Serenade to a Face in the Crowd.' I'm dedicating it to a special lady who's here tonight. Could I have a stool please?"

Carrying a guitar, he moved out from behind the keyboards, picked up the mike placed in front of him and sat down. He strummed a few notes on his guitar and looked up at Toni. Caught up in a storm of emotion, unable to think, she knew that the song was meant for her. She also knew that here, now, Cay was most vulnerable.

She knew why he'd insisted on singing this song out in front with the acoustic guitar. It was the only way he could relieve her of her responsibilities at the board and allow her the complete freedom she needed to listen and enjoy the song. He'd made himself vulnerable to Torgen because of her.

He began to sing, and Toni took the gift he had given her. She relaxed back on her stool and just . . . enjoyed.

His voice floated above the soft strumming of the guitar, and the lyrics were . . . wonderful. They were lyrics she'd never heard before.

You were only a face in the crowd to me,
A face from a lonely memory,
But then one day you stepped out of that crowd,
You came into my heart . . . and taught me to love.

Enthralled, she forgot to worry. Wrapped in the web of beauty Cay spun, she forgot to watch. The first clue she had that anything was wrong was the sound of murmurs coming from the audience, which until then had been quiet.

Her heart jumped and skittered. Torgen was swinging jauntily down the aisle, heading straight for the stage, wearing the same hat he'd worn the first night when they'd seen him on the street. Because he looked so outlandish, with feathers floating everywhere, the audience laughed, thinking it was part of the show. He was almost to the stage steps when Liz's hand moved toward the light switch.

"No," Toni warned. "Not yet. Wait till he gets up on stage."

Her heart pounding like a trip-hammer, Toni slipped the first tape out of the recorder and replaced it with the one that she'd had Cay prepare before the concert.

Torgen had almost reached the stage. Everyone was looking at the contrast of purple and orange feathers in his broad-brimmed hat, and no one saw the gleaming edge of the knife he held tucked by his side—no one but Toni.

"Toni," Liz gave a terrified whisper.

"Wait," Toni ordered tersely, her nerves dancing with tension. "Just . . . wait."

Torgen mounted the stage and walked toward Cay. "Your singing days are over, Sinclair." The knife flashed.

The laughter died. An unearthly silence fell in the theater.

"Hello, Torgen," Cay said in an easy drawl that carried over the microphone and was meant to calm the crowd. "Did you come to reclaim your guitar string?"

Torgen's mouth moved in a pout of feigned injury. "I don't know anything about a guitar string."

"I'll bet you don't."

The silence in the theater echoed in Toni's ears like thunder.

Torgen's arm came up, the knife in his hand.

"You should be packing a drumstick, not a weapon," Cay said easily, as if he were discussing the weather.

Torgen's arm wavered in midair with uncertainty. "I would be if it hadn't been for you."

"I'm not your enemy, and you know it. Your trouble comes in little white packets."

Liz, her face pale, whispered, "Toni!"

"Not yet," Toni said through gritted teeth. "He's got to turn a little more."

"But Cay's in danger. That creep's got a knife."

"I can see that. Cay can use the guitar to shield himself if Torgen moves before I can give you the signal."

"Oh, God, this is crazy," moaned Liz. "Why didn't I go to dog-grooming school like I was going to?"

"Be quiet . . . and keep your hand on that switch."

"You've sung your last song, Sinclair. Your swan song—"

"Now!" Toni ordered. Liz lunged, hitting switches quickly and methodically. The room was plunged into a darkness relieved only by the red exit signs above the doors.

There were cries and screams. Above the noise of the crowd, Cay's voice rang out. "Everyone stay seated. Don't anybody move." Then eerily, from the back of the room, he said, "I'm here, Torgen, come and get me."

"I'm over here, Torgen, come and get me," Cay said again, but this time he sounded as if he were dangling from the ceiling.

"What's the matter?" Cay's voice taunted. "Can't you find me? Come on, Torgen, come and get me."

Her eyes adjusted to the darkness, and Toni could see Torgen reeling around on the stage, trying to follow the sound of Cay's recorded voice as it spun out from different locations through the speakers. "Where the hell are you? Dammit, stand still—"

The tape played on, and Cay's voice rang out from center front stage. "Come on," Toni muttered under her breath to the cringing figure on the stage, "turn around just a little bit more. . . ."

Searching for the source of Cay's voice, Torgen pivoted slowly to face the audience. "Now," Toni said to

Liz, and a spotlight clicked on and blazed full in Torgen's eyes, blinding him.

"No," he cried. "No."

A police officer stepped out of the wings and disarmed Torgen. Liz hit the switch for the houselights, and it was all over. It took only a few seconds for the policeman to cuff Torgen and hustle him out of the theater.

Speaking to her across the crowded theater, Cay said through the microphone, "Toni, are you all right?"

"Yes, I'm fine. Except—" she forced her shaking voice to say the words "—I'd like to hear the rest of that song."

The audience clapped and stamped and whistled in wildly relieved agreement. Cay, bowing to majority opinion, returned to his place on the stool.

Like liquid pearls, the notes fell into the hushed quiet.

When it was over, Toni's eyes were filled with tears. She sat and listened to him sing three encores. At the end of the third song, his voice had begun to sound raspy, and he thanked the audience for their forbearance, apologized for any inconvenience, and after taking four bows, he strolled off the stage.

Liz and Tommy volunteered to strike the setup and do the packing. "Go on," Liz said, giving her a shove. "Go see him. I'm sure he wants you to be with him."

Toni didn't have to be urged a second time. She ran up the aisle and fought her way through the crush of people standing in the hall. The dressing room door was open, and the doorway was filled with people. A too-thin man of about her height, whose shirt looked as if he'd pulled it from the unclaimed lost and found bundle at a Laundromat, stood just in front of her.

"Fergy?" she said in amazement.

He didn't turn around; he couldn't move that far in the crush of people. Instead, he twisted his head and caught sight of her out of the corner of his eye. "Hey, brat. How goes it? Some concert, huh? Look, let's get out of here and go talk."

Over Fergy's head, she caught a glimpse of Cay's face. He looked drained and exasperated, and one of the women from the Key West Association was closing in on him. Toni decided Cay would have enough to do to get through the next few hours without worrying about her. "Sure, Fergy. Where do you want to go?"

Cay Sinclair stopped listening to the dowager who stood in front of him lavishing him with praise and staring at him as avidly as if he were a new car she was thinking of buying. Over the woman's head, he'd caught a glimpse of Toni's shiny black hair, tousled just as it always was after she'd spent an evening wearing headphones. Someone caught his arm, demanded his attention. When he looked up again, Toni had turned around. His lady was leaving, threading her way back through the crowd . . . with a man at her side.

FERGY WAS GOOD COMPANY. He always had been. Good company, but nothing more. When he offered Toni a ride home, she took it, thinking she couldn't stand to stay away from Cay any longer. She'd go home and wait for him there.

Fergy stopped the car in front of Cay's house and gave her a pat on the hand. "You're okay?"

"I'm okay."

"Yeah," he said, looking at her, "I guess you are. That was some song Sinclair wrote. Listen, call me if you need me."

"Sure." She got out of the car and walked slowly up to the house. She had a key, but she didn't get a chance to use it. As she put her hand out, the door swung open.

"Did you enjoy yourself?" Cay stood inside the door, looking exactly like a jealous husband. He'd showered away the heat and perspiration from the concert and looked cool in a white linen shirt and dark pants. No, he didn't look cool. He looked icy.

"Yes," she said.

"Another one of your admirers?"

"He's a friend."

"You're a friendly lady."

She fought to control her temper, knowing that his sharpness was part of the backlash from the tension of the concert and his confrontation with Torgen. Now wasn't the time to act like a rebellious teenager. Now was the time to act like the mature woman she was. "Thank you for the song. It was beautiful."

"There is one thing about it," he said dispassionately. "I can't take it back."

Despite her determination to keep cool, her temper flared. "Did you want to?"

"When I saw you walking out of my dressing room with another man after I'd stood up in front of two hundred and fifty people and told you that I loved you . . . yes."

Furious with him for saying the words she'd wanted to hear for so long in an icy voice, she said, "Is that what you did?"

"Yes, that's what I did."

"You're wrong about not being able to take it back." She reached into her large shoulder bag and pulled out the audio cassette. "Here. Consider it returned." She slapped it into his hand and whirled past him to fly up the stairs.

He found her in his bedroom. She was snatching her things from the drawer, dumping them carelessly on top of his leather brush-and-comb set, making an untidy pile of shorts and halters.

"You're not leaving." His voice came from somewhere behind her. She looked up into the mirror. The deadly quiet in the room made her nerves prickle.

"The day you put those things in that drawer, we talked about how we would settle future arguments." He was tall and dark and as still as water in a pool. Only his eyes held vitality.

Lifting her head to stare at the reflection of his tanned, chiseled face, she snapped, "Well? What's taking you so long?"

If there was a change in his facial expression, she didn't see it, but he grabbed her elbow and turned her into his arms so fast it made her head spin.

"You little spitfire. Lord, you're going to keep me busy." His eyes had an amused and possessive look as he walked her backward toward the bed.

"Am I going to keep you?"

He could see the question in her eyes. "You told me once I needed a keeper. Want to volunteer?" He bore her down and half lay on her.

She slanted him a dark glance and reached up to tap his nose. "I don't know. Do I want children who can stare down at me over this?"

"There's nothing wrong with my nose. All good singers have long noses."

"You should see it spotlighted in blue," she said, shaking her head. "If I didn't love you as much as I do—"

"But you do, don't you? So stop fighting it and kiss me, Sinclair," he ordered her.

"My name isn't Sinclair."

"Not yet. It's only a matter of time." Aware that she wasn't agreeing, he bent over her and took her mouth with all the satisfaction of an arrogant male. When he'd finished kissing her, he leaned away and looked down into her face. It didn't matter that she hadn't acknowledged his proposal. He wasn't finished yet. "That's better. Much better. I've been hungry for that ever since you gave me that excuse for a kiss in the dressing room."

"I didn't want to have the makeup man murder me."

"He's lucky I didn't murder him."

"Murder..." She shivered, thinking of the danger Cay had been in. "What about Torgen? What's going to happen to him?"

"I've given him a choice. He can either go for treatment, or I press charges. He's got twenty-four hours to sit in jail and think it over. I think he'll make the right choice. At this particular moment, I don't give a damn what he does." He nuzzled into her neck. "Did I thank you for thinking up the scheme that saved my hide?"

"No, you didn't. Rather ungrateful of you."

"Maybe we can work out a schedule for me to show you my gratitude—after we're married."

"Cay—"

"You were the one who mentioned children. And I want them, noses and all. I want all the things I've missed. But not until you've finished those two years of college. Why did you quit, Toni? Was it a man?"

"You are tenacious, aren't you?" She was still trying to deal with the heady joy of knowing that he wanted to stay with her for the rest of his life just as much as she wanted to stay with him. "I was expelled... for demonstrating against the administration. They had fired a woman unfairly, and there were a group of us who were trying to get her reinstated. Instead, we got ourselves tossed out. It wasn't fair...."

He looked down at her, his expression one of amused pride. "I should have known. You gave up your education rather than your principles. Lord, I didn't know there were people as honest as you in the world. I was so wrong about you. You'd be the last person in the world to betray me."

She glared up at him. "Well, it took you long enough to figure that out."

"But now that I have... I won't forget it."

She looked at his wonderfully dark, attractive face and knew it was true. He had learned to trust her. And she had learned to trust him.

Tracing a lean finger down her cheek, he said, "Will you mind if we have a small wedding, with just our families? Afterward, we can go to New York and you can settle in there—"

"I think you've forgotten something," she said in a dry tone. "If we invite my family, that automatically escalates it into a *big* wedding."

He gave a mock shudder. "You're right. But they'll surely want to be on hand to celebrate the wedding of the bed hog and her subsequent departure from the family circle. It seems unfair to exclude them."

"Unfair!" she cried. "You're the one who's unfair—" she reached for a pillow and whacked him with it for emphasis "—and ungentlemanly—" another blow caught him on the shoulder "—and unscrupulous."

He caught the pillow and disarmed her, his eyes brilliant with amusement. "I'm all of those. Especially unscrupulous. When it comes to doing whatever I have to do to keep you with me, I have no conscience." The amusement faded. "I'll always want you, Toni, and love you. Do you believe that?"

He'd gone deadly sincere in a microsecond. He looked eggshell vulnerable as he sat there braced, waiting.

Looking at him, letting her love shine out of her eyes to bathe him in its radiant glow, she said just as seriously, "I'm not sure. Maybe you'd like to convince me?"

She felt him relax. "Only if it takes me the rest of my life."

"Oh, it will, Cay. Believe me, it will. I'll see to that."

He was sure that, obstinate little perfectionist that she was, she would. "I'll look forward to every minute of it."

"Then how about starting now?"

"It will be my pleasure, sweetheart," he murmured, his mouth on hers. And it was his pleasure . . . and hers as well.

DESPERADO – Helen Conrad   £2.75

In this fast-paced and compelling novel, jewel thief and embezzler, Michael Drayton, has a five thousand dollar price on his head. With Jessie MacAllister after the reward and hot on his trail, the Desperado turns on his devasting charm, leaving her with one key dilemma... how to turn him in!

ONCE AND FOR ALWAYS
Stella Cameron   £2.99

The magic and beauty of Wales and the picturesque fishing village, Tenby, form the backdrop to Stella Cameron's latest poignant novel. Caitlin McBride's past reads like a fairytale, and returning to Tenby seems to offer the only escape from a dead marriage and hellish family life. But would the spell still exist – and would she find the love she had once left behind?

Published: DECEMBER 1989

W●RLDWIDE

Available from Boots, Martins,
John Menzies, W.H. Smith, Woolworths
and other paperback stockists.

TASTY FOOD COMPETITION!

How would you like a years supply of Mills & Boon Romances ABSOLUTELY FREE? Well, you can win them! All you have to do is complete the word puzzle below and send it in to us by March. 31st. 1990. The first 5 correct entries picked out of the bag after that date will win **a years supply of Mills & Boon Romances** (*ten books every month - **worth £162**) What could be easier?

```
H O L L A N D A I S E R
E Y E G G O W H A O H A
R S E E C L A I R U C T
B T K K A E T S I F I A
E E T I S M A L C F U T
U R C M T L H E E L Q O
G S I U T F O N O E D U
N H L S O T O N E F M I
I S R S O M A C W A A L
R I A E E T I R J A E L
E F G L L P T O T V R E
M O U S S E E O D O C P
```

CLAM	HOLLANDAISE	OYSTERS	SPICE
COD	JAM	PRAWN	STEAK
CREAM	LEEK	QUICHE	TART
ECLAIR	LEMON	RATATOUILLE	
EGG	MELON	RICE	**PLEASE TURN OVER FOR DETAILS ON HOW TO ENTER**
FISH	MERINGUE	RISOTTO	
GARLIC	MOUSSE	SALT	
HERB	MUSSELS	SOUFFLE	

HOW TO ENTER

All the words listed overleaf, below the word puzzle, are hidden in the grid. You can find them by reading the letters forward, backwards, up or down, or diagonally. When you find a word, circle it or put a line through it, the remaining letters (which you can read from left to right, from the top of the puzzle through to the bottom) will ask a romantic question.

After you have filled in all the words, don't forget to fill in your name and address in the space provided and pop this page in an envelope (you don't need a stamp) and post it today. Hurry - competition ends March 31st 1990.

Mills & Boon Competition,
FREEPOST,
P.O. Box 236,
Croydon,
Surrey. CR9 9EL

Only one entry per household

Hidden Question _____

_____

Name _____

Address _____

_____

_____

_____ Postcode _____

mps
MAILING
PREFERENCE
SERVICE

COMP 8